NIMROD INTERNATIO

MIRRORS & PRISMS

Writers of Marginalized Orientations & Gender Identities

ISBN: 978-0-9860178-7-2   ISSN: 0029-053X
Volume 59, Number 2
Spring/Summer 2016

THE UNIVERSITY OF TULSA — TULSA, OKLAHOMA

ADVISORY BOARD

Acknowledgements

This issue of *Nimrod* is funded by donations, subscriptions, and sales. *Nimrod* and The University of Tulsa acknowledge with gratitude the many individuals and organizations that support *Nimrod*'s publication, annual prize, and outreach programs: *Nimrod*'s Advisory and Editorial Boards; and *Nimrod*'s Angels, Benefactors, Donors, and Patrons.

ANGEL ($1,000+)

Lisa Ransom and David Flesher, Stephani Franklin, Susan and Robert Mase, The Ruth K. Nelson Trust, Office of Institutional Advancement at The University of Tulsa, Francine Ringold, Ann Daniel Stone, Randi and Fred Wightman, Jane P. Wiseman, The John Steele Zink Foundation

BENEFACTOR ($500+)

Raymond Feldman, Cynthia Gustavson, Kathleen Patton Westby Foundation, Rachel Zebrowski

DONOR ($100+)

Ellen and Stephen Adelson, Teresa and Alex Adwan, Ann Alspaugh, Diane Burton, Katherine and John Coyle, Ivy Dempsey, Patricia Eaton, Marion and William Elson, Helen T. Glenn, Laura Gonsalves, Sherri and Stuart Goodall, Frank X. Henke III, Nancy and William Hermann, Linda Jennings, Sam Joyner, The Kerr Foundation, Inc., Marjorie and David Kroll, Robert LaFortune, Carol McGraw, James Millaway, Constance Murray, Catherine Gammie Nielsen, Donna O'Rourke, Gloria Parker, Pamela Pearce, Judy Randle, Joan and Harry Seay, TD Design, Fran and Bruce Tibbetts, Linda Williams, Mary Young and Joseph Gierek

PATRON ($15+)

Margaret and Charles Audrain, John J. Azrak, Wendy Barker, Daniel Becker, Devika Brandt, Mary Cantrell, Robin S. Chapman, Suzanne Cleary-Langley, Marsha Cooper, Barbara Crooker, Kim Doenges, Linda and William Epperson, Nina Forsythe, Helen Diane Glancy, Kristina Gorcheva-Newberry, Ellen Hartman, Virginia Henshaw, Linda Hillringhouse, Marcia Hurlow, Carol S. Johnson, Susan Land, Susannah Lawrence, Lori Levy, B. D. Love, Maria Lyda, Geraldine McLoud, Wendy Mnookin, Linda Murphy, Terri Niccum, Brent Pallas, Keely Record, Earl Reineman, Ann Robinson, Alexander Runciman, Penelope Schott, Diane and James Seebass, Lynn Shoemaker, Andrea W. Slot, Lianne J. Spidel, Bruce Stoesser, Myrna Stone, Lee Upton, Ann Watson, Melissa Weiss, Kenneth C. Weston, Linda Woolford

Table of Contents

v

Editor's Note: Mirrors & Prisms: Writers of Marginalized Orientations & Gender Identities

Welcome to *Nimrod International Journal*'s Spring/Summer 2016 issue, *Mirrors & Prisms: Writers of Marginalized Orientations & Gender Identities*. Throughout our history, *Nimrod*'s primary goal has been the discovery and promotion of writers whose work has not been available to mainstream American reading audiences or who have not yet received the attention that they deserve. In 1973 we shared the work of writers such as Linda Pastan and Olga Broumas in our *Women in the Arts* issue, and in 1977 we shone a spotlight on the voices of African and African-American writers in our *New Black Writing* issue. In 1981 we published *Arabic Literature: Then and Now*, highlighting work from traditional and modern writers from across the Arabic world, and we did the same for writers from India a few years later in *India: A Wealth of Diversity*. It is when we share the stories and poems of writers with diverse experiences and unique viewpoints—writers whose voices have not been heard as loudly as they should be—that we are truly fulfilling our mission. So it is with great joy and excitement that we present *Mirrors & Prisms: Writers of Marginalized Orientations & Gender Identities*.

Mirrors & Prisms features the work of writers who identify as lesbian, gay, bisexual, transgender, queer, intersex, or asexual, or anywhere under the umbrella term MOGAI (marginalized orientations, gender identities, and intersex). While *Nimrod* has always published the work of such authors (and indeed James Land Jones, *Nimrod*'s founder, was himself gay and fought for gay rights in Georgia in the 1970s as a professor of literature), we have never before devoted an entire issue to LGBTQIA writers. To do so now, we believe, is not only to continue *Nimrod*'s tradition of bringing less-heard writers to the literary forefront, but to make clear what *Nimrod* has always known: that LGBTQIA writers have stories that can make a difference to all readers, of all sexualities and gender identities.

As with our recent issue *Lasting Matters*, which featured only writers age 57 and over, we decided to focus this issue solely on LGBTQIA writers. While we firmly believe that straight allies are vital, we wanted to give our writers a space entirely of their own, a space to tell their own stories. Additionally, focusing on only LGBTQIA writers allowed us to accept poems, stories, and creative nonfiction without regard for subject matter. In this issue, you'll find work on all subjects, rather than only stories of coming out, sexuality, and identity. To keep the issue open in this way was very important to us, as we wanted to honor the breadth and depth of writing by our contributors, rather than limit their writing to a single aspect of their lives.

Thus, we present an issue filled to the brim, one overflowing with prose and poems that reflect an exciting range of topics by writers from all walks of life and publishing histories, with our contributors ranging from those well known in the LGBTQIA community to high school students making their publication debuts. The *Voyager* spacecrafts take on an extraordinary new life in Jessica Rae Bergamino's poems of life, death, relationships, and space. Old stories of all kinds get a new spin as myth and math meet in Allen Salerno's "Orpheus Considers a Geometric Proof," a twisted modern fairy tale takes hold in Kelly Magee's "Nobody Understands You Like You," and Baba Yaga roams New York City in Charlie Bondhus's "Baba Yaga and the Book." The physicality of our lives stands front and center in Caroline M. Mar's poem "Body," while Eleanor Lerman takes us on a journey in the opposite direction in her story "The Life of the Mind." Love appears in all its forms, from that of brothers and sisters in Lucien Darjeun Meadows's "Following I-64 West" to the love of partners in Ellen Bass's "Kissing After Illness" to the lost love of youth in Shelley Ettinger's "Ginny Calabrese." Here too you will find tales of coming out, sexuality, marriage, and politics. Laura Jok explores the changing friendship of two teenage girls on the cusp of adulthood in "The Love of God"; Matthew Hittinger confronts what the DOMA ruling did and did not confer in his two poems; and Bonnie J. Morris describes her own experiences documenting the LGBT movement in "Writing in Women's Bars." And all this is just a sampling of the fascinating, assured, and compelling work within these pages.

I'll close by sharing a last thought. When we announced this issue, we hoped the response would be positive, but we had not anticipated the level of enthusiasm from writers across the country and around the world. And not only did we receive notes of general enthusiasm; rather, one of the comments that we saw over and over again was a thankfulness that *Nimrod* would decide to honor the work of LGBTQIA authors. The fact that so many authors expressed this same sentiment is, in our opinion, proof that issues like this have value, even as great strides are being made for LGBTQIA rights, and that the field of literature in general still has a long way to go to achieving full parity for LGBTQIA writers.

And now, I hope that you will sit back and enjoy the fine writing before you, in the way that it both mirrors the experiences of writers and readers around the world and displays a prismatic rainbow of new and brilliant voices.

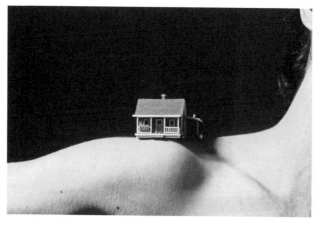

Ashley Inguanta, photograph

Ashley Inguanta, photograph

Mothman: Describes the Process of Metamorphosis in an Interview with The New York Times

Longer than winter but less mechanical than sex.

A river slowly ripping a hole in its own shirt of ice.
Something that keeps breathing
until it outgrows its own cage of bones.

Imagine the sound of wind around a single wire.

Imagine the sound snow would make falling
inside an amphitheater with no audience,
followed by a sudden fear of heights.

Flight is for actual heroes.
Truthfully, most of us can't tolerate that kind of loneliness,
and most of what comes after is just an endless huffing
about in the stadium lights.

I came into this world like every normal apple
with an untreatable longing.

Did I always know what I was?
I'll tell you what, I knew what I wasn't.

Columbus Day

When I arrive it's night, or almost night —
        a single small cloud hangs low over the prairie,
the foxes are out again, silver in the grass.

        On our way into town you pull over and point
to the last place you saw your father: a bus stop.
        A Guatemalteca, he named you after his favorite American

television reporter. His favorite place in Denver,
        an old movie theater called *The Mayan.*
In this country, hunger for one thing often becomes desire

        for another. I tell you, when she was eight, my great-grandmother
was taken from her village and put into a boarding school —
        at night she would run down to the river,

undress her dolls in the light of the moon
        and rub clay all over their bodies. Once a fish
swam up her leg and became a child.   That's a story I made up.

        Call me a priest, a medium, a tabloid. You know how it is,
in a language of stolen tongues, anything I say might be true.
        I'm like the Arapaho who told you:

for now, our strategy is to let them think they are winning,
        I'm in touch with the past in an attempt to get ahead
of the past. Sometimes I get a ghost in my ear.

        Sometimes the day ends without ceremony or crows.

Minneapolis

If I'd been a bit bolder there on that park bench
maybe I would have put my head in your lap and recited
something I'd written earlier, when you were just a thought
with no words attached to it. That summer the wind
brought down over a thousand trees, remember?
How their trunks lay open like legs in the too-hot night
but didn't make a sound? The quiet rested on your shoulders
and settled into the folds of your shirt—there was nothing
to panic about. On Tuesday you wore a suit,
on Sunday, we rode the bus. In between I scrubbed the sink
and retrieved a mouse from behind the oven, stuck my head
inside the freezer. I told the ceiling fan I'd wait to call
and then I started listening to music again, before it was just the news:
a ghost town hospital prepared to close, postmodern cowboys
convened a desert rendezvous. What haven't I told you yet?
Only the parts I haven't said to myself. I'd like it if you asked me
because then I could say, it's easy to be a beautiful thing
in the moment, harder over time. Down by the river
you showed me the old mills, where the new sits among the ruins,
where a few things have kept their names.

After the Storm

Belief is simply a cornering car, the assumption
       that the perpendicular street will be there,
       that it exists despite our not perceiving it.
Or maybe belief brings into being the road never there.
       Some philosopher—Berkeley maybe—said God
       must exist because someone had to be all-waking
or we'd be snuffed; not noticed means not there. Either
       way, we're none the wiser, either way reckless,
       counting cards in a hand without rules.
We downplayed the warnings, the alert crawling below
       the screen like an irradiated vein, the Pollockesque
       Doppler. No thunder, the rain a vague pulsebeat.
And we were right, there. Drama queens, to take flight
       at every threat, characters in those disaster movies
       they used to make, or the one about mutant bunnies.
Or mutant babies, there was at least one of those. The power
       didn't even falter. Except for one rush of wind
       (a handful of diced onion hitting a hot pan
and seizing) there was nothing else to rip the ordinary.
       The terracotta pots were russet-dry by dawn.
       So to see the beltway, four blocks away, littered
with the detritus of trees—fingers of kindling reaching and crossing
       and crooking across a mile of asphalt, like browning
       Christmas-tree needles wept onto a hardwood floor,
the tree hauled to the curb, a trail toward erasure soon itself erased—
       to see this was to fathom our escape, our vanity
       of dryness. Or our becoming there. The titles from the cinema
marquee were all blown off. Neighbors woke to foot-high letters,
       like the vestige of a mystical, unearthed language,
       scrabbling their lawns, created from our certainty
that we would be untouched, from our lack of words for doubt.

Matt, Home From a Run

Unvarying, the beeline to the bedroom
where he stoops to untie his shoes,
prising one off and levering the other
off with his toes. Summers, he tugs
his shirt off, too, standing bare-chested
in the doorway, his hair flattened
to his torso like a tract of turned earth.
Winters, he just unzips his jacket
and lets the sides flap, two light chords
unpinned from the music of internal heat.
Then to the kitchen for two glasses
of water in quick succession, derricking
before the counter on the balls of his feet.
I suspect he doesn't realize I have memorized
his patterns, would say, *you barely glanced
up when I came in.* He looks boyish
in the morning light, with his cowlick rebellious
against his neck. He rattles a tattoo
on his belly, less leftover endorphin
than a closet pride in its still flatness,
assurance he has kept another day in check.
His drying sweat as he passes smells
of neither sex nor labor but the damp sheets
after his fever broke the midnight
of his thirty-first birthday. He never
hops the creaking floorboard near
the bedroom door, and, missing that warped
squelch, I would find the silence menacing
and vast. In headier days, I would sometimes
follow him, still sometimes follow him.
Now I see him always. *Don't look
at your feet*, he chided when we ran
together, *look up.* So I wait for this moment
every time. I have looked up ever since.

Orpheus Considers a Geometric Proof

Given: they were separate points upon the line that connected them.
  They were pegs in the frame with the lyre cord between them.
  For any two points there may be only one line which contains both points,
    one frequency of music.

Earth and Hell were parallel, that was his folly, to suppose
  he could thwart this. He knows staves. But he also knew
  the mornings beside her, the algebraic flexibility of melody.
  So he imagines.

He recognizes the downward slope, the bisecting line; above and below
  it transverses, now and then, before and after twice over,
  for any two points on a plane, the line containing those points also
    lies on that plane.

Because they were so much the same, their luck was in separation,
  he at one end of that jagged road, she at the other.
  Alternate interior angles are congruent because on opposite
    sides, across the line.

He thinks of them as triangles, names their angles: Him, Her, Love.
  Prove the congruence: Him, Her, Death. The line between them
  contained by this plane, a side. *Angle Side Angle.*
    Death ≈ Love.

He tries again, names again. Him, Her, Death. Him, Her, Life.
  From the start, only one of them could have life. Or life itself
  would congrue to death. *Corresponding parts of congruent triangles*
    are congruent.

It was because he looked at her, he knows. The mind-game of the proof
  made that inevitable. Congruence lies in the folding of parts,
  shapes doubled over to stare at themselves. Riding their angles, they
    must come face to face.

If equals are taken from equals, what remains will be equal. And so
  the space between them remained unchanged. Not by fact
  he knows themselves in parallel diminishment, but only
    through proportions.

The grasses above have more complicated vectors, the crags and seas
more renegade equivalences. He feels the empty, soundless hours
gape and writhe in search of their own boundaries. Neither is grief
more orderly.

Ashley Inguanta, photograph

Eighty Beats

Suppose that time—
not death—is the frontier
that separates us. Maybe it is less of an abyss.
You could be close—an arm's length away—
but eighty beats of a hummingbird's wings
too fast for my eyes. Look! That dash of emerald,
that dip and whirr as swift as a neuron star's
spin could be you.

    Sometimes love slips
past the screen door like the neighbor's dog
in search of food. If there are chips in this world where spirits
pass through thin screens, slow this scene—let me live in the still
when you hover in mid-air to drink the honeysuckle in.
Let me be the flower jouncing in contrapuntal swing
to your nipping bill, your otherworlding wings.

Nocturne

Hung up like black crepe
commemorating the night's feast,
a throng of bats in single file, rump to rump,
doze the day away. When dusk falls
and night, upside down, becomes coercive
as a magnet, they stir, click, and split
from their perch in near-unison.
They are all appetite,
milk teeth and crooked fingers surrounding us
in our dreamtime: spirits on the bridges,
in the walls, atop the eaves.
If—half-awake—you were to stroke
one's back, its little bones
might remind you of grandmother's hand,
light and trembling in yours,
a squeeze away from breaking.
Some loves are like that:
pervasive, ravenous in their hour,
but clutch too hard, and they will shatter.
Even the blind know there is a terminus
out there in their periphery.

Nobody Understands You Like You

We encouraged her to get the dog. Not that we take respon-
sibility, because we don't, and the word we used was *puppy*,
by which we meant a retriever for the kids or a terrier she could
train to wave bye-bye, but she's one of those sanctimonious types
hell-bent on salvaging wrecks, so of course she went to the pound,
and of course she started with Death Row, and of course she chose
an animal no one else wanted. That no one wanted *for good reason*
is our point, but she didn't ask our advice. Never mind that we
shared twenty feet of chain-link in the back. Never mind the howling. We'd have told her to avoid anything high-pitched or hairy,
no googly eyes or missing legs, nothing elderly or special-needs,
and okay, pick an ugly one if you have to, but for god's sake, don't
bring home an animal that belongs in the woods.

We might not have thought to say, specifically, don't bring
home a wolf.

What she did was she brought home a wolf.

Claimed it was a mixed-breed husky, but no amount of
paperwork could convince us it was domesticated at all. It didn't
walk; it slunk. Army-crawled across the sidewalk. Patchy fur and
beady eyes, silver tuft between its shoulders that stood up like a
dorsal fin. The leash like an insult around its neck.

The day she brought it home, one of us—was it me?—whispered, *That thing has definitely eaten Grandma.*

Swear to god, right then every bird in the neighborhood went
silent.

We didn't confront her right away. Poor thing was a divorced
mom, no family or friends, and if she'd made a single good decision
in her life, we didn't know about it. Her ex was a real condescend-
ing type who once stole a snow shovel off our porch and replaced
it with an inferior snow shovel. We were glad she'd gotten rid of
him. We wanted her to heal and be the good neighbor we knew she
could be, inviting us over for dinner and whatnot, the kids clinging
to our legs when we walked in . . . we didn't have children, but we
thought we'd be good godparents, though we weren't entirely sure
what the job entailed, and anyway, we weren't trying to jump the
gun on the relationship, just that she was exactly the kind of lost

soul we liked to befriend. We had a whole bevy of lost souls in our rotating potluck, and they always brought the best cocktails.

We hoped if she ever stopped moping she'd see how she didn't need anyone else because we could mow her grass in the summer, and bring chicken soup if the kids were sick, and give her a cup of sugar if she was—well, she wasn't the cookie-making type, but you know what we mean—and that's the kind of neighborhood we wanted to live in. We could've taught the puppy to balance a biscuit on its nose, or—we're not opposed to thinking big—to do magic tricks like in that video that went viral. We could've been famous, and not in the way we are here, now, talking to you.

She was suffering. You hear stories about mothers who crack, and you always wonder about the bystanders, the family, the *neighbors*, and there we were, watching her unravel and telling ourselves we had to do something. We're not heartless. We worried about the children and also our property values. There had been a number of car prowls and a problem with graffiti, and we're not saying her oldest son was responsible, but we'd caught him in the alley more than once. So yes, we called Child Services. And yes, they did a home visit. And when she asked if we knew who'd narked on her, and when she explained how *that little curveball* was going to affect her custody battle, and when her tone got too snippy for us, we suggested she get a puppy.

But she brought home the wolf, and then instead of buying dog biscuits, we were stocking up on pepper spray to keep the thing from lunging at us every time we returned the gym balls her kids whiffed over the fence.

But now we're getting ahead of ourselves.

Those kids were trouble, it's true, but we admit to not entirely thinking through the whole Child Services thing.

✿ ✿ ✿

The day she brought home the wolf, we were at her door within the hour, holding the gift we'd made, a mug for her and a matching water dish for the puppy. Her eyes slid from one of us to the other.

"Greg," she said. "Linda."

"Hi, Jamie," we said.

She smiled. Well, smirked. Difference between laughing at and laughing with, as Mr. Fletcher, our high school band director, used to say. Band kids get picked on, which was why we stuck together. *You should get married*, he told us. *Nobody understands you two like you do.*

The wedding was perfect. We said our vows in unison.

That was almost thirty years ago. Sometimes, when the rotating potluck lands at our house, we break out the clarinets and play our wedding march from memory. We can also do the fight song and national anthem, and we take requests when our friends remember to bring sheet music. Jamie came once, but she drank too fast and clogged the toilet, and when this one guy, Clark, who always said what everybody else was thinking, asked her what she did in her free time, she pounced. "Time is always free," she said, raising a shaky glass. "When we stop believing that, we cease to be human." The glass tipped, and the wine went everywhere.

She declined all invitations after that, even though we told her the stain came right up.

We appreciated that she thought about what it meant to be human. When we got philosophical, our friends told us to lighten up, and that was disappointing because of the unexamined life not being worth it or whatever.

The day she brought home the wolf, Jamie stood in her doorway waiting for us to say what we wanted, so we started in, volleying back and forth and interrupting each other how we do: *congrats on the new pet, is it really a husky? big enough to be a guard dog, must be some kind of zoo reject, not going to lie, looks like a flipping wolf!*

"A wolf?" she said. "I guess a little."

Not judging! Not criticizing! But what's the return policy because it seems dangerous, frankly, and we're worried about you and the kids, which, where are the little hellions by the way, hellions in a good way of course, they upstairs?

"With their father." She slumped against the doorframe. "He gutted me in court."

We gasped. She frowned.

"It wasn't because of you," she said. "He dragged in my whole personal life."

We knew what that meant. A visit from Child Services was nothing compared to her personal life, which, truthfully, we didn't approve of either. Her new friends were worse than her ex. We say friends, but they were her lovers or whatever you call it. They didn't make polite company, so we didn't know their names, but we called the last one the witch doctor because she carried this old-fashioned medical bag for a purse and wore a fur coat—we're put off by the whole business, so we don't even want to speculate—mink?—and once we asked our friends what everyone thought was in that huge bag, if it was herbs or spells or body parts on ice, but Clark just said it was probably booze, and where was the fun in that?

The witch doctor is the one you heard about, but there were others. One had a yappy dog she kept in her car all night, parked on the street in front of our house, so we left a note on her windshield that we didn't appreciate the dog's noise, and the next day our lawnmower got stolen.

Another one kept knives in her glove compartment. Don't ask how we know. Not pocket knives, either; more in the category of weaponry. *Deadly weapons*, as Kip Clipson, the host of *America's Likeliest Criminals*, says, and if we're being honest, there were striking similarities between Jamie's new friends and America's likeliest criminals.

It was like Jamie needed to love things that were hard to love. Maybe that was her talent. Maybe that was her downfall. It was definitely her downfall, but maybe it was what she needed to survive. Like she dealt with pain by summoning it. If not pain, then danger. Maybe she thought she was being proactive, inoculating herself against real tragedy.

She wasn't. But we admire her for the thought, if that was her thought.

※　※　※

Is it wrong to say we expected better because she was a mother? We'll put it this way: Jamie was no victim. We're not saying she got what she deserved, but we want you to know it's not like it sounds. She took unnecessary risks. She fostered tendencies in herself she would've done well to suppress. We thought a puppy might convince her to act less like a sex-crazed lunatic. We hope you don't mind if we're blunt about that. It's not like we *want* to say these things. We liked Jamie. She was good people, as Mr. Fletcher used to say. She was solid.

But she left her windows open when she and her lovers were going at it—they called it *fucking*, if you want to know, and we didn't think that was appropriate in a house with children—and we don't think she even owned curtains.

Sometimes, listening to them, we'd kiss each other and promise never to be mad. Sometimes we got a little frisky ourselves and wondered what would happen if we let loose like that. We didn't really want to find out, just that they seemed so grateful to be alive and young and naked, and don't get us wrong, we love each other, but we're not young anymore, and we certainly never walked around naked. We've also never had to call the cops on each other, so there you go. It was like living next door to this great movie. Maybe it makes your life seem smaller, but once it's over, you're grateful to be back in your car and headed somewhere familiar.

Jamie never knew where she was going. She needed stability. We thought that even if a puppy didn't help, it couldn't hurt. Boy were we wrong about that.

To be fair, she didn't get a puppy. We want to be very clear about that. We never suggested she get a wolf.

❊ ❊ ❊

We told Jamie we were sorry about the custody thing, and she invited us in for tea, and we would've gone in, we absolutely would've, if the wolf hadn't right then skulked up behind her. Fixed us in its evil gaze, tongue lolling. It looked at our necks and salivated. She'd tied a red bandanna around its neck, which she took in one hand while she stroked its back with the other. Its expression didn't change or soften. Just meeting its eyes rearranged your soul.

We told her we didn't want to intrude, that we'd talk another time about the wolf.

She smirked again. It was hard not to take offense. "You really think my dog is a wolf." Like she was making note of it.

We backed off the porch, calling our goodbyes from the sidewalk. Jamie petted the wolf hypnotically, muttering, "Goodbye, neighbors."

We tried to talk to her about the wolf on three other documented occasions, but she refused to listen. We've been asked why we didn't call Animal Control, but you have to understand that the thing *came from Animal Control*. It's not like vigilante justice is in our natures. We were band kids. We preferred dinner parties to stakeouts.

We even called our Realtor, Sue Singleton, and she did a walk-through but advised us to hold out until spring. "I'd call someone about that dog next door," she said when she left. "It's real off-putting."

We started unlatching Jamie's gate. That's our confession. Maybe it wasn't right, but we felt trapped. We wanted the wolf gone, and we didn't care how it happened.

Meanwhile the thing with Jamie got worse. The witch doctor was there whenever the kids were not, and we'd seen Jamie throw the witch doctor's clothes on the lawn, and we'd seen her lie in the snow while the witch doctor tried to persuade her to come inside, and we'd seen her drink a whole bottle of vodka and then vomit off the porch, and we knew she was falling apart. Domestic violence is wrong, and we were pretty sure Jamie was getting the brunt of it. It made us jumpy and exhausted. We never knew when they might have an outburst. Once the witch doctor pounded on our door, and when we didn't answer, she waved her hands around like she was either casting a spell or swatting bugs, but we were pretty sure it wasn't bugs.

"Perverts," she yelled. "Stay off our property." Which was a weird thing to say since it wasn't her property, and all we'd done was politely knock and inform Jamie that we'd seen the wolf stalking somebody's cat across from the Dairy Queen two blocks over.

Before she left, the witch doctor kicked a pot of our begonias off the porch. Jamie was over sweeping terra cotta shards before we could call the police, so we didn't call them, though, in retrospect, we should have.

"Sorry about that." Jamie wore the red bandanna around her head. "It's been hard."

We kept it short: *You deserve better.*

"I know," she said, nodding, but we could tell she didn't.

Later, Jamie and the witch doctor walked to the ravine at the end of our street and stayed down there a long time. Hours. When they returned, Jamie was wearing the fur coat, and they had the wolf back on its leash. Her ex dropped the kids off that evening, and the witch doctor made a huge meal that they all ate in the dining room like a regular family. Jamie set out a bowl of food for the wolf, but it looked like it'd just as soon eat her face.

Something bad is going to happen, we said to each other. Jamie's problems had become our problems. We talked about what we needed to do. We agreed that nobody was going to help us, but we were in this together.

You pulled out one of those weekly sales fliers, folded around an ad for a tent sale at Gun World.

I thought that was your idea.

Anyway, we went together.

❊ ❊ ❊

We know what this sounds like. It sounds fake, right? The wolf, the witch doctor? It sounds like we're making this up to get on TV.

We'll take a lie detector, if you have one.

❊ ❊ ❊

The marquee outside Gun World advertised training classes and party rentals. We browsed the pink and orange Swiss Army pens in the tent out front before heading inside. The place was packed. A guy in a white button-down swiped our driver's licenses at the door and directed us to a waiting area, where a girl in an identical button-down shook our hands. "I'm Brittany," she said. "Is this your first visit?"

We nodded. Brittany wore a lot of mascara. She told us she was a psych major at Eastern and had four older sisters, which explained the mascara. She listened attentively to our story, frowning like she was used to hearing bad news.

"Nuisance animals compose a large chunk of our business," she said. "We know the value of a peaceful home." She folded her hands at her chest. "I'm a yoga instructor here, too."

Here? we said. *How wonderful and surprising!* We asked what we should do about the wolf, although we called it a dog. We didn't want to alarm her.

"I can't advise any particular course of action," she said. "But I can show you some options."

We told her that options were exactly what we needed her to show us.

She led us to a roped-off section where demo weapons hung on the wall like athletic shoes. They had names: Happy Ending, Last Resort, Old-Fashioned. One of us modeled the First Timer in a three-way mirror while the other compared Hustler Pro to Hustler Comfort. We eliminated anything too complicated or cheap. Brittany was encouraging but discerning, talking us out of the flashy Rorschach and the nostalgic Western. She recommended the Problem Solver for our needs, and we appreciated the ease of its point-and-shoot operation, as well as the handcrafted holster. Brittany guaranteed our satisfaction and signed us up for a marksmanship class on Mondays and her own Yoga for Stress Reduction class on Wednesdays.

"It's for every body type," she said as we left.

❄ ❄ ❄

On Mondays we learned how to aim and fire, and on Wednesdays we meditated on a world where our problem no longer existed. Brittany wore a headset and asked us to imagine how it would feel to live in a stress-free world. She asked us to consider what we could do to eliminate the stressors in our lives. We peeked at each other and the cross-legged people around us, an older woman in sweats, a lanky man breathing loudly. We pictured them solving problem after problem like superheroes.

We appreciated how the class increased our ability to empathize.

At first, the presence of the Problem Solver really did seem to solve our problem. Jamie bought a padlock for the gate, and the witch doctor built this elaborate doghouse in the backyard. She had the kids out there hammering and painting and putting little candy-striped curtains in the windows. Jamie put down mulch in the front yard, even planted a couple of hot pink Gerber daisies. We would've picked something less ostentatious, but we were glad she was finally trying to fix the place up.

We felt okay, and even went ahead with our night of the rotating potluck. That was when one of us—no, it was you; I never would've done that—brought out the Problem Solver for the first time. Clark said, "That's frightening," but everyone else seemed impressed. You pointed it out the window at Jamie's house, where the wolf was standing in the window, staring at us as usual. The rest of us laughed nervously until you pulled back the hammer. "Play dead," you said.

The beast stared, unmoved.

"It's not loaded," I said, and you said, "Yes, it is."

You dropped your arm, the Problem Solver by your thigh. Said you needed to take a shower.

I said, "Right now? In the middle of the party?"

You raised the gun and pointed it at me.

Our friends tutted around, *come on now* and *that's not funny* and they poured more wine and made jokes—*tough guy, eh?*—but they could tell I was shaken. You cracked a smile, finally, and said, "Just teasing."

But you sort of said it to the room, not to me.

Then you went upstairs and took a shower.

Later that night, you climbed on top of me, and I could've sworn your eyes glowed. We did it every night that week. Can we say that? It's true. You smacked my behind once. You'd never done that before.

I thought you said you liked it.

I never said I didn't like it.

❁ ❁ ❁

We were so caught up in each other, we ignored what was going on next door, which is a shame because the next week was when all hell broke loose.

We've traced it to the doctor's bag. Seemed that Jamie, like the rest of us, was curious about what was in it. So she snooped, and whatever she found upset her. We heard them before we saw. We were walking back from the Dairy Queen, where you'd put my hand in your pocket, and I'd felt the Problem Solver there. I hadn't known you'd brought it, but I kissed you right there on the sidewalk.

"You guys are so cute," a girl watering her lawn told us.

My hand was still in your pocket when we heard the yelling. We knew right away who it was.

"That's private property," the witch doctor barked.

"You lied to me," Jamie yelled.

And so on.

We weren't sure what Jamie had found, but there was a skirmish on the lawn, and at one point Jamie dumped the bag. We got a glimpse of ripped envelopes and tiny liquor bottles before the witch doctor scooped everything back up.

"You bitch," the witch doctor yelled.

Something was going to happen. We could feel it in the air, even before Jamie's son came outside with the wolf. Jamie told him to go back inside, but he picked up a handful of mulch and threw it at her. Hard as he could, right at her head. The wolf jumped around like it was delighted, then it broke free of the leash and leapt right for Jamie's throat.

We could say we only meant to scare them. That's what people say about situations like this. But that would be a lie. We felt calm. Our blood pressure was normal. We didn't want to scare anybody. We wanted to save Jamie.

You took the gun from my pocket.

But you were the one who'd brought it.

I always wondered what kind of person I'd be under pressure, and now I knew.

You were flipping amazing.

We were. The car prowls stopped after that.

You knew right what to do. Didn't you? Didn't you know exactly what to do?

I did.

And your aim! Blam: problem solved.

Shout-out to Brittany at Gun World.

The poor kids, though. They were traumatized for a good long while, though we're sure they're okay by now, or at least we haven't heard otherwise. The thing we'll remember forever, though, is how Jamie held that damn wolf after it died. Everyone froze at the explosion of the gun, and it was like nobody wanted to move again to see what damage was done. The witch doctor held her bag like a shield to her chest. We never saw her again after that.

The wolf's head was blasted open, but Jamie, god bless her, crawled over and gathered that creature in her arms like it was her baby. Stroked its horrible side. Buried her face in its fur. That woman—she generated hope like a force field. Rejected the label *vicious dog* to the end, though that was the official verdict.

We never could explain to her that she didn't have to deal with all that transmutation of pain. We heard she moved into an apartment complex with a gated entry and a no-pet policy.

Our new neighbors are a young couple in some buzzword science field we can never remember, bookish and waifish, the kind of people who reminded us of ourselves just starting out, before houses became things to stage, lists of interchangeable amenities and spin. Before we learned how to spray-paint and spot-clean. The day they moved in, the sun was setting behind the house in a way that covered the roof in light and made it seem holy, like the end of a movie. The trees were still as cardboard.

Welcome to the neighborhood, we said. *Let us know what we can do.*

A. Gannon, photograph

Borders

There are always intruders.
The moth who dives down my blouse
after midnight. The alcoholics,
on their porch, knowing if I come or go.
The Gregorian chants which somehow start
playing from my phone during staff meeting.
Pema Chödrön wants to ask
what these invasions bring us,
to welcome them.
I want the moth to die.
Or I want to feel its flutter of flesh
in my palm. Or I want it to turn
into a butterfly and teach me this limbo.
Look! I've plucked the wings off.
This isn't the night I unscrewed
the ceiling light to let the gnats out.
This is letting them burn, crushing
them in cumin with my pestle,
shaking them into my hair.

Anatomy

My body is a temple. Just kidding.
My body is the abandoned psychiatric building

off North St. My sister and I climbed through glass,
walked past piles of molding patient files.

We wanted to see the view.

Her body was a path. His body was a shadow.
Her body is every woman I've known.

The thing about bodies, his body told mine,
is they're designed to break.

Tongue swollen in the ghost of my throat,
I was fluent in phantom by sixteen.

My first cousin is midnight. My second, mosaic,
ceramic, smashed against college dorm walls.

A collage of phone calls from my mother,
asking, *How's your sister?*

She is. I am. We are.
Star. Carbon. Snow.

Semicolon

I.

A pause indicating
two connected clauses;
two thoughts strung on a
wire and hung around a throat to lie
just in the divot; the place
where if you really wanted
to choke the heat out of someone,
you would press your thumbs;
if you wanted to make
them bleed, that's the X that
marks the spot; if you wanted
to feel breath you would focus
all of your energy on that point
only to be disappointed; the place
that hollows when you swallow
hard, adjusting the
pitch of your
voice.

II.

I know you
never thought you would
identify with a punctuation
mark; with what always felt like
an unnatural pause, air hissing;
when you were a kid and would exhale
until you couldn't anymore just
to watch your chest
become concave.

I know that you felt
complete, whole, like a person;
I know between what ideas
you placed your semicolon;
I know you've heard it before

when you would push down
on your fingernails; comb your
hair to one side; fasten the top
button so it lies just in the divot.

They're just asking you to stop;
for the love of god,
stop.

Girl

"Let me" she says/ pushing my fingers away/
wrapping the fabric around my waist/

tucking it against my hipbone/ too tight/
tossing the rest over my shoulder/ pinning my blouse/
scratching my skin/ sighing at my rigidity.

"Breathe in"/ pushing at my back/ then at my stomach

I picked out the fabric but I don't remember it being this coarse

"Soft" she says/ pushing at my shoulders/
smiling into my face/ until/ I smile back/
smoothing the petticoat/ turning me/ to face the rest

"Girl"/ she repeats/ over and over/ /my stomach hurt

Origins of Dress

"Wait. Could you explain it to me?
I really want to understand."
—SCM

transitive verb

1 : to make or set straight

"Just because you're a lesbian doesn't mean you need to dress like a man."

2 : to prepare for use or service; *specifically* : to prepare for cooking <*dress* a salad>

People often joke that my high school was a finishing school in disguise. I'm not sure I agree with this, but when I enter my parents' home and see the photos from those years staring back at me, the vertigo is overwhelming. For our graduation, we each wore a long white dress and carried a dozen long-stemmed roses.

I loved my high school, I truly did. I loved the people I met, who remain some of my dearest friends. I had many wonderful memories during this time of my life. So why does it sting so much to see that girl—who was me, but feels so far away from me—look back at me in all those dresses, in all those frames?

3 : to add decorative details or accessories to : <u>embellish</u>

"He said he's not paying $30,000 for a wedding for the bridesmaids not to wear dresses."

4a : to put clothes on <*dress* a child>

It was a graduate playwriting class in my second spring at Columbia and I was my usual early. We sat in a dingy, fluorescent-lit rehearsal studio-turned-classroom where we transformed a couple of plastic folding tables into desks. The professor was who I imagined "Dear Sugar" to be when she was still anonymous. Fifties, married, with a store of brilliant stories of SoHo in its grimy, artist-filled yesteryear. With her son fully grown, she and her husband were in the midst of moving from the Jersey suburbs back to the city, and thus clearing out massively to fit their lives back into a one-bedroom Manhattan apartment.

"Do you wear ties?" Her eyes were round and earnest, her question kind. I felt caught. My face blazed red.

"I never have, but—it's not that I haven't thought about it . . . "

"Well, my son had all these amazing vintage ties. I was planning on giving them away, but why don't I bring them to you?" She paused gingerly, attending to my response with a gracious smile and a casual flip of her wrist. "You'd be doing me a favor. If you want them, great. If not, just get rid of them."

b : to provide with clothing <feed and *dress* a growing family>

It was the Fourth of July weekend at a family-sized cabin on a lake in southern Maine. A dear friend's family owns a music camp in the area and is generous about visits, so another friend and I eagerly joined for the holiday.

A retired Broadway producer who once read a play of mine happened to be in town and invited the three of us to dinner. The restaurant was casual—your typical lobster joint—but he was a man to impress. Unfortunately, I hadn't brought many clothes for the days away.

"You can borrow one of my dresses," said one of my friends. We've known each other since we were ten and grew up together as Catholic school girls in New Orleans, Louisiana. Despite having lived in New York for nearly ten years, she is still *very* southern and *very* Catholic when she wants to be.

"No," I replied, feeling a surprising ache rise through my chest. "I haven't worn a dress in years. I wouldn't feel comfortable—"

She peeled off her sunglasses. "That's ridiculous! Why not? Just wear the dress."

I remember most that painful crack in my throat when my voice amplified, my jaw tightly clenched, my eyes gathered their forces against tears. The rest of the memory is a cloudy blur, like a puddle of milk that disappears into your coffee. We didn't make sense to each other, and I wondered if we ever would again.

5a : to apply <u>dressings</u> or medicaments to <*dress* a wound>

"You are *not* wearing a dress in that wedding." My therapist glared at me, hard. She is quick to laugh, but a smile was a thousand miles from her eyes in that moment. I've been her patient for nearly four years and we've long deliberated over this topic, but this day felt bigger, stonier.

I received a package from a friend sweetly asking me to be a bridesmaid in her wedding. Before I even opened that piece of priority mail, I let it marinate on my kitchen table. She had announced her engagement months before. I knew what was inside. Not exactly, no—but I knew what it would lead to. I felt my breath get shallow, I showered, I prepared dinner, I answered emails, I avoided it as one does uncomfortable conversations. After all, this package would be one monstrous conversation piece.

At last, I tore the package open—in one swift motion, like ripping a Band-Aid from a fresh wound. Her letter, written on the first page of a beautiful new Moleskine notebook, was incredibly moving and I was honored to be considered, yet there I was, wracked with anxiety.

The words *Will you be my bridesmaid???* in her familiar handwriting gnawed at the edges of my thoughts. I was sleepless, and I couldn't understand. *It did all seem ridiculous*. It did seem like it could be so easy to don a dress for a few hours for the sake of someone I loved, for the sake of *her* day. I always imagined I would do just that for my best friends' wedding days and I always imagined that it would be no big deal. So why on earth was this small, insignificant detail so difficult?

b : <u>cultivate</u>, <u>tend</u>; *especially* : to apply manure or fertilizer to <*dress* a field>

"It's HER day, NOT YOURS." The same childhood friend with me in Maine two years before spat across the table during a reunion with another buddy from home. This was her reaction when I revealed the recent call I had with my bride-to-be friend about not being able to wear a dress to her wedding. "You *will* be in my wedding and you *will* wear a dress!"

It was late and we were waiting for our food at a small Latin-American restaurant in the East Village. Drinks had by all, except me—who was remarkably sober for Lent. Four of us were New Orleanians, and a fifth, a successful New York-based musical theater performer. The actor barked to our mutual friend in my defense: "What if I decided to show up to your wedding in a dress, huh?"

While I appreciated the ally and the thought, I wasn't sure his argument actually added up. A) He would be uncomfortable and out of place wearing a dress and shouldn't be forced to wear what he wouldn't feel comfortable wearing? Or, B) If I wanted to be a woman in a suit, why couldn't he be a man in a dress?

Suddenly, I regretted saying anything. Why had I said anything? After all, she was right.

My male New Orleanian friend looked at me like a small boy for several moments before speaking. He might as well have been wearing his Jesuit uniform from days of old. At last, he spoke. "But I don't understand."

And while I launched into a reply, while I parsed together some version of explanation as best I could, I couldn't entirely understand it either. It was a feeling, a deep-rooted feeling, a pulse that echoed through my body, an instinct. But how do you explain instinct?

c : to kill and prepare for market or for consumption —often used with *out*

My eyes drifted to the dresses in the back of my closet. They had gone unworn for many years, but I couldn't let them go. Every time I gathered another batch of clothes for Housing Works or the latest donor-bag left at my doorstep, I let them remain in their safe haven beyond my daily wardrobe of collared shirts.

❈ ❈ ❈

One night, I got very drunk with friends. I stumbled into my apartment, tore my closet open, and stuffed the dresses into a plastic bag. It felt like a strange, secret crime.

"I almost wish you would have burned them," my therapist offered.

6 : to align oneself with the next soldier in a line to make the line straight

It was an appropriately sticky summer day in San Antonio, Texas. It was hours before the ceremony, and the bride was having her makeup and hair done in the choir room. The bouquets arrived and I, along with the "wedding coordinator" at the Baptist church, brought them to safety in a nearby bathroom.

"What does your dress look like?" The coordinator offered in her patented Texas drawl. She seemed more like a cartoon, or at least a sitcom personality, than a real person. I had built myself up for this moment even before the plane ride and felt my feet lock into the ground.

"I'm actually wearing a suit."

She puckered her lips, squinted her eyes, and gave an overly polite nod of her head. "Oh, well isn't that *interesting.*"

noun

1 : an outer garment (as for a woman or girl) consisting of a one-piece bodice and skirt

"What color dress are you wearing?" My father asked over the phone when he learned I was to be the maid of honor in my dear friend's San Antonio wedding. While in many ways he's the farthest from a macho Cuban baby-boomer, he is still a man of his origins and his generation.

My San Antonian friend asked me to wear a suit almost as immediately as she asked me to be in her wedding. "I can't even imagine what you would look like in a dress anymore," she told me—and I was very grateful.

Still, on the phone with my father, I lied: "It's mint green."

"Wow. What a color, huh?"

"Yep."

I replied with the color of my dress shirt because I didn't want to start another argument. It didn't seem worth it, for either of us, and for the first time, I didn't need him to tell me it was okay.

2 : apparel, clothing

I was invited by the woman I was seeing to her cousin's upstate wedding. When my mother called, I prepared myself for another hour-long volley about what I would wear and why.

Instead, we talked for a while with no word on the subject. Just before closing the conversation, she offered, "You know, I was looking at the weather and it's going to be very cold up there."

This is it, I told myself. I took a deep breath, ready.

And then, "Make sure you wear a nice blazer."

3 : covering, adornment, or appearance appropriate or peculiar to a particular time

When people ask me why I rarely act anymore, I tell them, "Because once I realized who I was, I didn't have the desire to dress like anyone else anymore."

4 : a particular form of presentation : <u>guise</u>

The last time I tried to wear a dress was for a theater festival's awards ceremony my first year in the city. It was a test for myself, in a way. To prove that I could do it. I wanted to show myself and the world that I wasn't some lesbian stereotype. I was still a woman, after all.

But while I may not have been a stereotype that night, I wasn't genuine. I felt like someone else, like a ragdoll with a buzz cut, moving aimlessly through the city—and I never wanted to feel like that again.

You Ask How

You ask how and I tell you about the fire,
that day every soft spot lit up

in the deep under-skin of my interior.
My look too long into the eyes I'd loved

since 7th grade. Lips pinked
and glossed, legs urgently shaved—

the rapidly emerging sex
of our bodies, meant only for boys,

later men. You ask how
and I say: cup tipped on its side,

empty of itself; angel hovering
above her own numb flesh;

walking, until I couldn't tell waking
from sleep. You ask how and I tell you

about the centipedes I had seen
in the night. Reality pressing through

my dream eyes. How I awoke
to find them alive—antennae to tail—

along the white crown molding
of my bedroom. You ask how

and I say: small word forming
in my mouth, in my body,

rising through limb and gut.
The man, the dream, the man

in the dream. How many times
had I seen this already? The man

to whom I am saying: no.
By morning, only the sticky remains

of a spider's home, sufficiently
abandoned. You ask how and I say:

cavern and ceiling and mind that is
home now to shaman and mystic —

where air flows into aperture,
and out of the darkness emerges

your own wild face.

Ashley Inguanta, photograph

First Memory

I remember the sidewalk.
The way it narrowed,

the way my father, years later,
taught me how to draw a road.

Wider at the bottom, narrower
as I moved up the page,

the lines getting closer and closer,
never meeting. How long it was,

cutting straight down the middle
of their yard, narrowing as I looked down it

towards the house, towards the stroller.
Never would have happened if she'd stayed home,

people said. The lines getting closer
and closer, never meeting.

(*She* being the mother. It was the seventies.)
I remember the sidewalk.

Not the sound of the phone
that must have rung,

must have been answered.
The lines getting closer and closer.

I remember the sidewalk,
not running with my mother

through our yard, through the alley
that separated our yard

from theirs. Me on one edge,
Katherine on the other—both of us

fixed into position. I remember
the sidewalk, not the look

on the housekeeper's face,
not the body, inert, inside the stroller.

To show distance, he would say.
Wider at the bottom,

narrower as you moved up
the page.

David Mondedeu, *Fugue of the Blackbird*, photogravure

Omniscience, Prayer, Pantheon

A woman dreams of birds—
sudden flock across a blue wake—
as her god becomes
the quarrel, becomes
confusion and descent. She dreams
of atoms that won't be still,
of Lucretius, of pleasure,
and the nature of things. The sun's
green flash, the five notes
of a whippoorwill. She sings
about the eye that rises
and falls, billowing as if body
and sky are one. A woman
dreams of rain—knows
she was made for ruin—
its muscle sweet to her skin.

I Meet a Woman

Friday night, after a long day of work
and far away from home, I am at
an event to hear a friend speak
and sell her books. I am tired.
Exhausted really. All I want
is to return home to my lover,
our dogs, our life. Then, across the room,
I see a woman. The kind
I always desire: butch,
wearing a gorgeous suit,
curly dark hair atop her head
(I can only imagine what is below),
confident, smiling, bewitching.
All night, from afar, I watch her;
finally, as the crowd dwindles,
we speak. She flirts,
marvels at how young I am.
Reader, I am not young, just
younger than she, and then
only slightly. She touches my face.
My face! I giggle. I am young enough
for such girlishness but old enough
to know: I want my hand inside her.

My desire reminds me of this lesbian myth:
two women are making love. One
puts first a finger inside the other,
then two, then finally her full hand is
inside the vagina of the other—
it slides in easily to the warm, wet,
engorged cave—you know how open
we become desiring, wanting, having another.
Then, when she comes, looking into
my eyes, the eyes of the other woman,
when she comes, she comes hard,
the contractions of her strong,
wet, vaginal muscles, squeeze

and squeeze so hard
a finger breaks.

It's a myth but in this moment,
I want this woman to break my finger.
I think about her for days. How
my hand might fit inside her, how
she might enjoy it. How she might
touch my face again when she comes,
my whole hand inside her loveliness,
drenched and pulsing. How we might
both be young and giddy, breaking things
while we come again and again.
Then, how if I see her again more will break
than a finger, how our carnal sex would destroy
more than a small digital bone, fractured
or shattered. If I see her again
we might destroy many lives.
I want to lay my hand inside her.
I want her to break my finger.
I want to break.

Math's Punishment

For Lucas

This is how I want to know your body—

In the *Mabinogion*, book of Welsh folklore,
the conjurer Math punishes two men, nephews
who had violated the woman whose job it was
to cradle his feet as he slept.
Math banishes the men to the woods for a year,
and with a wave of his wand transports them
into new selves: into stag and doe—
their hard uprightness melting
to haunch and hoof.

One year later, the barking dogs
call Math back to the castle gate
to find stag, doe, and behind them now, shyly,
a fawn. Math kneels, beckons it forward,
and when he lays hands on it, it flashes
into a sturdy boy of twelve, blond, the book says,
and Math leads him in to be christened
Hyddwn, which means *Of Deer*.
And the nephews? It must have glimmered

in them then that they'd once been men,
a dilating human awareness—
the doe apprehending with a man's grip
the spaces in her body, what the other
had filled—quick-fire, unexpected wholeness—
and the life that had crowned there
like a secret passed between them
now telegraphed to the world.
And the stag, too: recalling a man's body

as his own had been, fallen to all fours
in front of him, the press of his hooves
on its back, how it drew him from himself

into its sheltering vortex, the haunches
he desired and continued now to desire, that
were and were not those of the man he knew.
But Math isn't done with them yet.
He returns to the gate, raises his wand,
and tumbles them back into the world

for another year, the stag rolling
into the body of a sow, what was pendant
drawing sharply back, and the doe
lifting itself up as a boar, all energy channeling
through and outside itself, and both animals
charging out to thicket and plain
to exchange knowledge, to pass it between
them in a language of grunt and muscle.
Another year goes by, and again

barking dogs call Math to the castle gate.
And there, waiting for him, are sow and boar,
and behind them this time a young pig—
which he kneels and beckons forward.
At his touch, it, too, flashes into an upright boy,
whom Math christens Hychdwn, *Of Pig.*
Then he raises his wand and
—perhaps it comes slower now, a calculation
checked and re-checked, a sum which can't be

but is right—the nephews find themselves
upright, human. Math declares their experience
a great disgrace, and they stand beside each other
naked and public as a vow, each scraped
bright, mud-covered; each with the crazed
beards and hair of hermits. In a daze, then,
they follow him back to the castle.
The gates shut. And the *Mabinogion* isn't
much concerned with them after that.

But is there, lover, in any other mythology,
a pair like them?
Fallen and shamed, no doubt, but maybe

feeling something else, too—satisfaction, even
buried pride as they sit together at table
beside their sons, men in a family of men?
I think, none at all—
though maybe Adam and Eve come closest
as they stumble hand in hand out of Paradise

just as the nephews must have
stepped forward, if a little too stunned
to hold hands, away from the animal world.

Ashley Inguanta, photograph

Baba Yaga and the Book

The pavement hurts her
legs and she's sick of elbows
that bump and knock as she wanders
the Lower East Side, hungry,
and starting on a headache, so
when the light from the little shop
window reaches out like a bird
offering its wing, Baba Yaga
descends the concrete steps
and tugs the door.

Now she's in a modest secondhand bookstore.
Iron teeth blossom
from dirt-colored lips as she smiles
at the girl behind the counter,
so much like the pretty Anastasias and Yaroslavas
who have come to her chicken-legged hut
seeking counsel.

And yes, Baba Yaga always knows,
or if she doesn't, she has something
that will help—a charm, a trick,
an enchanted bit of fiddle-faddle—
things to loan out, and never see again.

Baba Yaga thinks she'd like a book
but what's the use?

She passes the military section
and thinks about the swords tattooed
to the inside of her skull, war a thing
she understands, having been in two,
or perhaps three. Fiction she never cared for,
all those pathetic characters
with fates predetermined
by the fashions of a century;
and why would she read history?

She notices the bright white
spine of a book sticking
just a little bit
out
of the shelf like
a young and reckless woman's jutting hip.

Her fingers clutch
the crinkling dust jacket
as she recognizes
women's words — like finding
something essential she doesn't
remember having, a talisman
or tool invented
in a previous life.

The shop's canary lights dim
and the girl behind
the counter yells, "five minutes,"
and the city traffic
swishes like a broom.

Outside, the streets and their people
ramble like the aimless
centuries. Baba Yaga feels
the weight of the book
in her hand, thinks
she hears the rustling
of some divine being
passing by,
but no,
it's just a flock of pigeons
taking flight.

Baba and I Klatsch Over Reasons Why We Hate Magic

The smell.

It only works if someone else asks for it.

Teenage girls in black nail polish.

It's the only thing that separates me from the animals.

After I cast a love spell, mosquitos follow me for days.

Candles get expensive.

I also play the guitar, but you didn't know about that, did you?

Men think it's sexy at first.

Never knowing whether I'm being asked for a hex or sex.

Concerns about sustainability. A finite resource, like water or time?

It's always a hex.

What would happen if big pharma caught on?

At the end of the day, it's just another form of housekeeping.

It never works on me.

Guilt Keeps Us Busy; Violence Makes Us Creative

I asked you to scrape the bathroom,
and you painted a Turkish
bath scene on our bedroom ceiling. You wanted
a gun rack to store your hunting rifles
which were sprawled across the kitchen table
like centerfolds, and I built a jungle gym
for the little boy who lives at the end
of the cul-de-sac.

We tried talking it through but power
tools interrupted, the circular
saws ululating in their grooves, heralding the arrival of Jesus
Christ, who said there's no greater miracle
than the cordless drill. *You see boys,* he explained,
*God IS electricity. I spent centuries in wine
since it was a place to sit
still (alcohol being a poor
conductor), but then came the lightbulb
and for the first time in 2000 years, I was visible
and useful.*

Sometimes we see the boy
biking in the neighborhood and it leads us down
that unproductive path of whether
we should've had children, and is it too late now?

Guilt keeps us busy; violence
makes us creative.

Whenever we feel like denying
the Lord, I flip
the switch and you
shoot out the light.

Lent

I gave up masturbation—
I thought it would bring me closer
to an orgasm that would make God
come from my lips like a hushed prayer
under my breath. I'd give him praise
like the pastor said, as if he actually lived
in the cavity of my chest
pounding away at the walls
of my left and right atriums, my striated
doors pulsing as he shouts, *Listen!*
If anyone hears my voice and opens the door,
I shall come unto him and dine
with him, and he with me. I imagined
he looked like Gil, the pastor's son
who was Jesus in the Easter plays,
annually hanging on the crucifix
revealing his abdominals like two sets
of knuckles pressed together, the way
a person can measure two human hearts.
It looked painful, Gil's body tearing
down the middle like that, his torso
ready to rip open and expose
his lungs as a pair of perched doves
inhaling blood and exhaling
salvation through tightened throats.

Photograph of Our Shadows

Hunched like the lightning-
split across this crevasse of sky, our bodies
against each other behind the lens, kiss
light beyond this universe—
some physicists believe
we can return to the cemetery,
talk about death with a sweetness,
and I'll hear you whisper, *Steven,*

struck tree, our shadow is
absent, but our mouths touch
almost like two black holes inhaling
our last photo together. Remember
every possible universe exists—
open a bottle of Barefoot Moscato,
taste apricot and peach on our tongues,
come back with me to the car,

it's getting cold out here.

The Anatomy of Your Voice

Only you can hear the rattle of bones
inside your voice, the skull's tenor

tucked around the alto of your vocal cords
like the drumhead of a tambourine,

the dense beat of a palm striking skin.
At ten years old you hear yourself

on an answering machine and realize
why kids call you fag—your vocal cords

aren't strings on a cello and aren't steel-
braided cables suspending a bridge,

they're membranes slit in your throat
like silver zils in a tambourine ringing

whenever you speak.
                    Remember to inhale

as if through the gills
on either side of a shark—

seven and seven, two halves of a sonnet
that can turn an ocean into breath.

A Boy With Baleen for Teeth

My father wished
        to cast me back-

wards caste and all:
        a wrong catch,

swaddled in dreams,
        saffron amniotic

dripping off my black
        whalebone gown.

   ❁

My baleen burst through
pursed lips. When I smiled

Sunday's Lutherans gasped
then laughed to hide

horror with *he will outgrow it.*
I opened my jaws

and sucked the plank-
ton from their eyes.

   ❁

My father's pliers gripped
        my plates and he etched
the story of the son he wanted

        onto my keratin. I gouged it out
and into the channels smeared
        India ink, and plunged, a fallen

star into the abyss.

❁

What to make of deep silence
that swallows the body, crushing
brown boys with its tongue —

     what a fool I was, drawn to any glimmer.

A whaler tore my dress then stuck
me with his harpoon after we kissed
in a haze of chanteys and Cutty Sark.

     I wanted to taste any body that shines in the dark.

❁

Night pulsed from the clouds
in nested song and I was rain too,

starved for seasons, breaching
at dusk: a silhouette

on a darker sea —
for seasons I was faceless

trying to swallow constellations,
to roll a star-map on my tongue.

❁

Once when lunging
     into the moon the sea

showed me my face
     as I trembled midair.

Stars shone through
     the holes of my body.

Skin and Hide

Skin

So the boundary is alive.

Hide

So the skin doesn't break
against every wave.

Skin

So the self is not the whole.

Hide

So the whole is not the whole.

Skin

So others have several
layers to pass through,
by diffuse force or
sudden invitation.

Hide

So the skin has several
skins, reservoirs
sprung up together,
spilling healing into hurt.

Skin

So an organ can play
at just barely willing,
walling, or welling in
a systematic wilderness.

Hide

So the shifting interior can be
worlds below sweat and perfume;
oil-painted, marl-soft,
and insight-specific.

Skin

So there's an overall contour
to tour, a seamlessness
to wander, bending
with its bones.

Hide

So the earth curves around
the tour and the tour
doesn't end with the skin's
being lost or sloughed.

Skin

So we have a place to attend,
our own surface, ice-thin
and just as grazed.

Hide

So we end up a pelt cut
from desire and disgust,
furring the line between.

Undertaking

If I were no longer able to write, but
wanted still to be near words, I would apply
for a job in paper-funerals direction

at the Western Wall: to be a person whose job is
to remove the prayers visitors have placed
in the Wall's time-widened holes,
then lay them into plots to be buried
like verbal cadavers, or seeds:
a person whose job is

to care for inscriptions asking
for someone else's care;
to pick up after faith's,
years- and year-long harvest;
to concentrate vast, varied, and
inscrutable hopes in a restbed, a respite

for words, the precise moment of whose
disintegration or germination
no one will ever know.

The Life of the Mind

It's August, hot as Hades, and—fully aware of what she's do-ing—Mary Orbach is flying straight into the path of a hurricane. Not that you could tell by looking out the window of the airplane, which is on its way from Indianapolis to Newark; outside, there's just blue, blue sky and whipped cream clouds, the skyscape of a dream. *Well,* she thinks, *the weather will probably hold for the funeral, and then I've got the hotel room for as long as I need it, even if the flights back are canceled.* She had checked that before she left, confirming that she could keep the room if she needed it for an extra day or two. At home, in Indianapolis, she had also checked the satellite weather channel early this morning, before she called a cab to take her to the airport, and had seen the swirling mass of the storm, depicted in TV graphics as a pulsing black whirligig—a wind en-tity, clawing its way up the East Coast—and determined from the information made available to her that she was going to be ahead of it, all day. She was confident that she had thought things out and planned her trip well. As well as you could, when everything you're doing has been set in motion by the fact that someone has died.

The flight is uneventful and the plane arrives on time in Newark, where she drops off her bag in her room at an airport hotel. Without lingering, she goes right back downstairs to catch a cab. Shortly, she is riding along a New Jersey highway that passes alternatively by strip malls and huge, belching factories brewing up God knows what kind of alchemical stew of fire and gases that singe the atmosphere, tainting it with a yellow haze. Occasion-ally, there are a few houses on a hill, hawks circling a patch of dry woodland. In other words, the scenery of Anywhere, USA.

The cab drops her off in front of the funeral home in less than half an hour. She passes through the glass entry doors and immedi-ately sees familiar faces—cousins, their children, assorted friends, and, of course, her Aunt Alice, the widow of her Uncle Jack. He was in his eighties and had been fighting colon cancer for a long time.

Jack was her mother's younger brother, and everyone here is from her mother's side of the family. Mary hasn't seen any of them in a couple of years, but since one of her cousins had some time ago set up an email list that included everyone in the family and sent out news about birthdays, graduations, new jobs, and all the things that family members care about (or should be expected to care about), she knew when Jack was dying, and she knew about the arrangements. What she doesn't know, isn't sure of, exactly, is why she's made this long trip to attend his funeral, though she imagines it's a matter of respect. She is aware that she's the distant one in the family, the odd one—not estranged, exactly, but certainly not part of this tight, loving group who both compliment and quarrel with each other on the emails that she sees, just as they do, have done, in real life, all their lives. Still, she grew up in the same apartment building in Brooklyn with her aunt and uncle and various other relatives, and now, fifty-some-odd years later, she still remembers, and believes in, these rules of her upbringing, at least: that the adults take care of the children, and the children acknowledge the sacrifices that were made on their behalf. She is Jack's niece, he was a kind and friendly man, and she should be here to participate in this last rite of passage.

Mary finds her cousin Ari, the one closest to her in age, and he greets her warmly. He's bearded, genial-looking, wearing a velvet yarmulke bordered with silver stitching.

"Well, hello, professor," he says.

She taps him on the head, touching his skullcap. "Very dressy," she says.

"My father would have loved it. You know how he was: the cheesier the better."

Mary sees his eyes tearing up and she says, "How are you? Really?"

"He had longer than we expected, so what can I say? But I'm glad you came. You should stay with us tonight," he adds. "We've got plenty of room."

"I booked a hotel," Mary tells him.

"Of course you did." He smiles at her and says, "See? I know how you are, too."

He leaves her then, drifting off to talk to other relatives. Looking around, Mary sees that her Aunt Alice is standing by the glass doors of the funeral parlor, gazing out into the bright afternoon. She walks over to her aunt—who, in her seventies, is still pretty, still animated by some inner liveliness of character, even under these sad circumstances—and murmurs her condolences.

Alice thanks her but continues to look out into the sunny day. Mary follows her line of sight and sees a car drive by, a big, boat-sized Impala that pulls up to an empty spot near some shrubbery at the side of the funeral parlor and performs a slightly jittery job of parallel parking.

"It's amazing that he's still driving," Alice says.

"Who?" Mary asks.

Alice gestures toward the car. "That's your Uncle David," she says. "He's ninety-two. Still driving, still teaching. Still brilliant, of course—but. Well."

Mary knows what's implied in that "well"—still eccentric. Another odd man out.

She watches as an elderly fellow in a short-sleeved white shirt and the kind of pants that must be sold in an old man's store—brown gabardine, belted somewhere around the breastbone—makes his way slowly toward the entrance of the funeral parlor. Can that really be her Uncle David? He's really that old? He walks with a decided stoop, and his beaky nose, always a prominent feature, now seems to be a heavy burden to carry on that old face.

"He used to be the only one who could deal with you," Alice says.

Mary is startled by Alice's comment, which seems to come out of nowhere. Actually, she's more than startled—she isn't sure how to process the information, or even respond. "What?" is all she says. "What?"

"After your mother died," Alice says, "you were impossible. Your poor father had to go to work and your grandmother tried to take care of you, but you drove her crazy. The only person you would listen to was David."

Standing next to her aunt, Mary feels as if this otherwise perfectly nice, sane woman has gone into some kind of trance and is summoning images from an alternate reality, one that bears some resemblance to Mary's own memories but has been twisted or corrupted in some bizarre fashion. *Her poor father?* Since when has anyone in this bunch referred to her late father in such kind terms? To begin with, her mother's side of the family always blamed her father for her mother's death when Mary was ten; they thought he didn't get her to the right doctors, he didn't fight hard enough with the doctors he did get when they told him that the cancer they'd found in her liver was inoperable, untreatable. And what was that about her being *impossible*? What did that mean? She remembers being angry, certainly—her reaction to her mother's death was not grief, not for many years, but total, raging fury; she was an aggrieved party, an abandoned child, deserted, deprived of love and care since her father, who was devastated by his wife's death, barely spoke to Mary for weeks afterwards, months—but *impossible*? What did she do? Break things? Scream? Hit people? Maybe she hit her grandmother. She doesn't remember, but she can imagine that she might have done that. She can imagine pummeling that big, doughy woman with her little fists. It was an impulse she had had for a long time, about a lot of things, a lot of people. But those feelings eventually drained out of her, or else she just learned to control herself. To channel her emotions elsewhere, as she got older. Into work, eventually. Into thoughts, ideas, writings. The life of the mind.

David finally reaches the door, pushing it open with his elbow, and comes in from the sun. But he seems to notice no one as he shuffles past Mary and her aunt, heading towards the viewing room where Jack has been tucked into his open coffin decorated with a veteran's flag. Mary excuses herself and leaves Alice's side to follow him.

She finds him standing in front of the coffin, staring at the chalky, wasted face of the body within—the shell of a thing that is now so clearly, deeply empty. The life of the body, life of the mind—all gone forever. Flown away, perhaps; perhaps simply finished, done. Somewhere in the background, some vaguely Jewish music is playing. It sounds to Mary like a soft, persistent wail.

"Uncle David," she says. "Hello."

He keeps his eyes fixed on the coffin for another moment and then turns to Mary. She isn't sure if she sees any recognition in his face.

"It's me," she says. "Mary."

Does he know her now? Maybe, maybe not. Mary can't remember the last time they actually saw each other. David says nothing but turns back to the coffin.

He is a brother-in-law, David, a relative by marriage. He was the husband of another of Jack's sisters—a perpetually ill woman who died decades ago—and the father of a trio of strange children, lost cousins, all girls, who disappeared into cults or moved to India; changed their names, their religion, their citizenship. For a long time, they have been on a trajectory away from him; they have, for all intents and purposes, left the known universe, never to be heard from again. What that did to him, no one seems to know. He is, as Alice implied, an eccentric man, and also phobic, possessed of perplexing beliefs. For example, he had his wife buried in an above-ground mausoleum, in a water-proof container of some sort, because he feared she would not like the damp. And for years now, he has pulled away if anyone tries to touch him. And he won't touch doorknobs. If there is no one on the other side of a door he has to walk through that won't yield to an elbow, he simply waits until someone turns up to let him in. This, then, is the only person that she apparently had an affinity for when she was an angry child. David, who lived on the top floor of the apartment building in Brooklyn. A professor of applied and engineering physics (not that anyone in the family understood what that was), who studied during the day, accumulating degree after degree, and taught at night. She does remember that, seeing David wander off in the evening, heading for the subway on his way to school.

Since he hasn't acknowledged her, Mary is about to walk away when he suddenly starts talking. He says, "Where I teach, whenever someone is getting a posthumous degree, a colleague is asked to accept it for him. That colleague always shows up in shirtsleeves, without a tie. I don't know the reason, but I always thought it was a sign of respect. That's why I showed up in shirtsleeves today."

Even his stories are odd, Mary thinks, but of course, they always were. If there was an affinity—and all right, there probably was—that was part of the reason. He was different from everyone else. He was smarter, stranger.

"I teach too," Mary says, just in case he has forgotten.

He makes a sound like a snort; cranky, dismissive. "I know," he says. "Infection."

For a moment she thinks he's belittling her field—always the academic's first reaction, she realizes—but quickly understands that he was annoyed that she'd think he didn't recall her profession. Smoothing things over, she nods, agrees. "Yes," she says. "Public health. My main interest is epidemiology."

He nods too. "Water-borne diseases," he says.

Mary is surprised: there is only one reason he could have brought up that specific subject. "You read my book?" she says.

It was an important book, often cited lately because of the rash of natural disasters in recent years that led to whole populations being exposed to tainted water. But still, you wouldn't exactly find it displayed on the front counter of your local bookstore; it was something you had to be interested in even to know it existed. Or be interested in the author.

"It's all very fine," David says, "but you should have concentrated more on viruses. Not bacteria; they're just opportunists. But viruses—they're chameleons. Every time we think we've got them, they roar right back. They've got the keys to the kingdom, all right." Finally, he makes eye contact with her. "You know that, don't you?" he says.

And yes, Mary does know—at least she knows this is his view—because he told her that once. He told her lots of things. That there might be dimensions of reality other than the one we live in; that television broadcasts, though they dissipated over time and space, would go on rocketing though the solar system and beyond for a period that might approach infinity; that aliens might have visited Earth. And when she was twelve and had the measles, which he explained was caused by an organism called a virus, he also told her about the theory that viruses were really the dominant life form on earth and that human beings existed only in order to provide a living laboratory for them, a reservoir of blood and nutrients they could swim around in while coming up with new ways to change and mutate whenever they needed to.

"I'll remember that," Mary says to her Uncle David. He snorts again—maybe this has become another one of his mannerisms, something he may not even realize he's doing—and says, "You never got married, did you?"

"No," Mary admits, wondering if he will think this is because she is still impossible, even mean. Cold-hearted. Is that what anger does? Can do? Chill the heart? The thought crosses her mind that she might explain to him that getting married was never one of her goals. That sort of thing is for the kind of people her cousins are—nice, friendly, loving, all that. Interested in each other, interested in the community and in family life. Mary thinks that over time, however difficult she may have been as a child, she has achieved some semblance of peace and of stability—but perhaps the price has been that she has remained at something of a remove from the kind of life it seems that the rest of her family have made it their business to achieve.

She is thinking of how to frame a reply to David, how to defend herself, when he makes any response unnecessary. "Probably for the best," he says to her, and then wanders away.

Soon, someone from the funeral home herds everyone into the viewing room. Then the coffin is closed, and short, loving speeches are made about the deceased. His children remember him with fondness; his friends tell jokes about him and recall how hard he worked all his life, managing a variety of small businesses that kept the family solidly, and contentedly, in the ranks of the middle class.

Afterwards, they pile into cars and hired limousines that take them to the cemetery, where they drive through the narrow, leafy avenues of the dead. When the line of cars finally comes to a stop, they all step out of their vehicles, smoothing their skirts, adjusting jackets, and pulling out sunglasses from purses and pockets.

The mourners follow the men bearing the coffin up a slight gradient and then along a hedge until they come to her family's plot, purchased nearly a hundred years ago by Mary's grandfather with pennies paid into the account of the burial society he belonged to. That's what they did, the immigrants from Russia, Poland, Slovakia, Slovenia; even if they could barely come up with the rent, they paid on account for ground to bury their bones in; someplace, finally, to rest. In this plot, her grandfather is buried next to his wife and their daughter, Mary's mother. Their other daughter is the one stored in a place where the dampness won't creep in and disturb her. Now, their son is joining his parents.

As a rabbi prays aloud beside the grave, behind him, in the distance, the hot sky is turning the deep, dangerous gray that precedes a storm. The air grows ominously still. It feels like banshees will begin howling at any minute. When the rabbi finishes his prayers, he invites everyone to form a line and, if they wish, participate in shoveling dirt on the coffin, which has been lowered into the grave.

Mary hangs back but watches as her cousins and their children and many of Jack's friends pass the shovel to each other and tip in a pebbly portion of earth from the mound at the side of the grave. One cousin in particular—a nephew from Alice's side of the family; a big, brawny man in a sweat-stained suit—digs into the mound as if it were part of a construction site and tosses in shovelful after shovelful of dirt, as if it is his duty to bury his uncle all by himself. Nobody tries to stop him; they watch respectfully as he grunts and groans, wrestling with spade and earth.

As she's observing all this, Mary notices David walking towards her, making his way through the small crowd. When he reaches her side, he makes that grunting sound again and then asks, "Where's your father?" His tone makes it seem like he's inquiring after a guest who is inexcusably late for a party.

"He's not buried here," Mary explains, though surely David knows this? "He's buried in Brooklyn, with his second wife."

"Marcia," David says. "I never liked her."

"Neither did I," Mary replies, which is an understatement. "She wasn't very smart."

Now, almost despite herself, Mary is amused. She understands that this is probably the worst thing David could say about anybody. "No," Mary agrees. "She wasn't." And, Mary recalls quite clearly, Marcia didn't like the fact that Mary was. It was like too much had been asked of her when she was handed an unusual child to raise, a difficult, intelligent girl who read books all the time and excelled at school. That kind of girl was always hanging around the house, studying; her education involved filling out lots of forms for special classes and consulting with teachers and guidance counselors, all of which apparently made Marcia the second wife feel stupid. And raised a troubling suspicion: did it mean that the first wife had also been a bright bulb? The effort of trying to replace a smart woman who died young seemed to have been an ongoing irritant for her successor.

"He got so mad at me that one time," David says. He has zoomed off to another subject and Mary has some difficulty following him for a moment, until she realizes that he hasn't gone far. He's stayed within the family circle. He's talking about her father.

"Why?" she asks. "What did you do?"

"That time we got stuck on the fire escape," David says. "Don't you remember?"

Yes, Mary does remember, though she hasn't consciously thought about the incident in decades, probably. "I do," she says. "But what were we doing out there?"

"I was watching you," David says. "I had to go out onto the fire escape and I told you to stay inside the apartment, but you followed me outside. And as soon as you climbed out onto the fire escape, the window slammed shut."

He hasn't really answered her question, but as the details come back to her, Mary can answer it herself. "You had a short-wave radio," she says, "and the antenna was attached to the fire escape."

"The super was always trying to make me take it down, but I wouldn't," David says. "And that night—it was the height of the Cuban Missile Crisis—I needed to adjust it because it was beginning to get dark earlier. I was trying to pick up any broadcasts that might be coming from the American blockade."

"Because of the ionosphere," Mary says, remembering what David had explained to her back then. "Its reflection characteristics are different at night, when the sun is down, so radio waves can travel farther."

David nods in agreement, one professor confirming the statement of another. Clearly, he's not surprised that she has this information at her fingertips. Whatever the source of her knowledge may be, he apparently believes that, as an intelligent person, she should understand the qualities of the atmosphere, have a working knowledge of the vagaries of time and space, and be familiar with compensatory measures required to deal with the curvature of the earth.

"It was a scary time," Mary says, remembering how really terrifying it was. One image that comes immediately to mind is the television in the living room in Brooklyn, of a program interrupted by an Emergency Broadcast, and the screen suddenly showing a black and white map of Florida, a long lozenge-shaped blob sticking off the end of the U.S., with Cuba lurking mere inches away. *Well,* her father said, *it looks like Daddy will have to put on his soldier suit again.* Her mother had only recently died and the prospect of being orphaned by imminent war sent Mary into hysterics. Her father tried to tell her he was joking—even if there was a war, he had already served in The Big One and was too old to be drafted again—but she didn't believe him.

"Even afterwards," she says to her Uncle David, "all those nuclear tests the U.S. was performing, and the Soviets, too. I used to think I could taste Strontium 90 in every glass of milk I drank."

"That's exactly the problem," David says energetically. "Everybody was looking to the skies, as if that's where disaster was coming from. First it was fallout—people actually thought you'd be able to touch it, taste it, as if radiation was going to drift out of the clouds." Inwardly, Mary feels herself shudder, envisioning a rain of poison cornflakes. "Then," David continues, "everybody was seeing aliens, remember? All you had to do was look up at night and someone would say, 'Hey! What's that?' Most of the time it was just some satellite.

"You're in the right field," David continues, sounding more subdued now, thoughtful. "Infectious disease. Once we got rid of polio and thought we'd figured out influenza, we had the idea that we were home free. But your friends, the viruses—they always knew what they were doing. They snuck in again, didn't they, with a whole new round of surprises. Drug resistant TB, HIV, Ebola— and that's just the beginning. I'm sure of it." Suddenly, he veers off into another subject. "I'm giving a lecture on Friday," he says. "At the college. You should come." With that, he turns abruptly and walks away.

The nephew who has been shoveling dirt into the grave sends a last spadeful into the ground and decides he's done his service. When he too turns away, the rabbi announces that the service is concluded and that everyone is invited to another cousin's house nearby to eat and begin the traditional seven days of mourning.

Mary rides to the cousin's house with some distant relatives who are pleasant to her, though they seem to have only a vague idea of who she is. Shortly after everyone has arrived, a half-hearted argument breaks out among Jack's three daughters about whether or not there is enough food for the mourners, though of course there are mounds of sandwiches, piles of chips and cookies, oceans of soda, wine, and beer. Various husbands are dispatched in cars that head off in different directions to bring back more cake, rye bread, fruit. Overheated children cry for ice pops; the family dog eats whatever the children feed him from their plates. Mary watches all this—*family life*, she tells herself; *this is one way that it goes on*—as she walks through the rooms of the house, noting the mirrors covered with sheets, the pictures turned to the wall. Eventually she realizes that she has been looking for David, who is nowhere to be found. He has apparently gotten into his Impala and driven away.

Mary soon follows. After saying her goodbyes, she calls a taxi that takes her all the way back to her hotel near the Newark airport. On the way, the driver keeps the radio on and Mary listens intently to its warning that the hurricane, which was supposed to weaken over land, has only grown stronger and continues its rush up the coast. Who could argue that danger is not imminent? The sky is turning blacker and the radio reports that flights into and out of the area airports are grounded. As Mary arrives at the hotel, it begins to rain.

Inside, you wouldn't know that anything is amiss. The hotel is a self-contained world, temperate, polite, anonymous. And all the lighting is subdued, as if movie stars hidden behind sunglasses might suddenly swan by, pretending to crave privacy. Instead, of course, the hotel is mostly full of business travelers. Mary rides up the elevator with a trio of suited executive types clutching briefcases, chatting about a conference they've attended. When Mary exits on her floor, the gentle music that had been playing in the lobby continues to float down the hallway as she finds her keycard and enters her room.

She unpacks a few things, changes her clothes. The she turns on the laptop she's brought with her and goes online to look up her Uncle David, something it's never occurred to her to do before. When he said that he was giving a lecture at "the college," she wasn't sure which one he was referring to, but a few minutes on the computer reveal that he is still teaching at the same school from when she was a child, the same school, apparently, that has always been his real home. The New Jersey College of Science and Engineering, in Newark, lists David Gerstein as a professor emeritus. Someone has even built him a webpage—every professor, even the adjuncts, seems to have one—where his old, beaky face peers out at her from a small corner of cyberspace. Other than his degrees— he is a City University of New York graduate, all the way—and his long list of publications, there isn't much information about him at all. Neither the deceased wife nor the absent children are mentioned, and if he has won honors or awards, few are included, though Mary is interested to note a brief break in his academic career that took place a few decades ago, when he seems to have taken a job as a consultant for NASA. But either that work— whatever it was; no specifics are given—was not to his liking or it just didn't suit him, because shortly thereafter he was back at "the college," where he has remained ever since. His affiliation there has lasted more than sixty years.

After Mary turns off the computer she watches television for a while, though as the night goes on, the programs are constantly

interrupted by local weather updates. She has the curtains drawn
in her room, which looks out at the undistinguished flatlands of
New Jersey, but she can hear the rain slamming against the windows. And the banshees *have* begun to howl: the wind has a voice
now, and it's screaming at what the red scrawl at the bottom of the
TV says is 70-plus miles an hour.

She falls asleep after watching the eleven o'clock news,
which is full of blurry footage of ambulances and police cars racing
around the streets of New York City, just across the river, and of
reporters in yellow slickers clinging to telephone poles and parking meters as they shout descriptions of what is eminently observ-
able to anyone in the vicinity with ears or eyes: the hurricane has
arrived.

Just before nodding off, she thinks about her apartment back
in Indianapolis: a few rooms, full of books, in a development that is
part of a complex of buildings that wind along a concrete walkway
bordering a man-made canal. This faux Venice, which cannot be
faulted for pretending to be anything else, provides tranquility. At
night, Mary falls asleep smelling deep water, watching the shadow
of cool water created by glass-globed streetlamps shimmer on her
ceiling. Here, in New Jersey, as Mary sleeps, she dreams about
death. In the brief awakenings between what seem like episodes of
a connected narrative, she is not surprised that this is the subject
occupying her dreaming brain. Not only has she spent the day at a
funeral, but her uncle's passing has reminded her—as if she needed
reminding, at her age, an unimaginable fifty-seven—that death's
approach is as obvious as bad weather. It is stalking everyone,
everywhere. It is the thing waiting around the bend.

Sometime before dawn, when the dreams are gone, Mary
is awakened by what she thinks is a man shouting in her ear, but
turns out to be an intercom system broadcasting through the rooms
of the hotel. A voice that is noticeably straining to sound calm is
instructing the hotel guests to evacuate their rooms and gather in
the hallways, away from the windows: there is a concern that the
hurricane-resistant glass may not hold up if the winds strengthen
even more, as it seems they are predicted to. As she jumps out of
bed and hastily pulls on a pair of jeans and a t-shirt, Mary clicks on
the TV and sees that the ever-present scrawl at the bottom of the
screen is now reporting that the hurricane has escalated to Category 2, with sustained winds of over 100 miles per hour. It is capable,

apparently, of uprooting trees, peeling back roofs, and producing other kinds of severe structural damage. Mary looks across the room at the curtains hiding the tall windows that, at the moment, are all that stand between her and the hurricane, and moves a little quicker.

In a few minutes, she joins the other guests on her floor, who are all huddled in the hallway. Here, it's almost impossible to hear the raucous wind, and since the background music is still playing—now Mary recognizes an instrumental version of a John Denver song—the sense that nothing is wrong keeps trying to assert itself. But how much can you deceive yourself? Hanging out in the hallway of a hotel with a bunch of strangers is not normal. Mary sits down on the carpeted floor and tries to make herself comfortable. She thinks about going back into her room to get something to read.

"Do you mind if I sit here with you?"

Without realizing it, Mary has closed her eyes; she may even have drifted off for a few minutes, but when she hears herself spoken to—by a normal, female voice this time—she looks up and sees a young woman, blonde, wearing a bathrobe and slippers. She looks very frightened.

"Sure," Mary says.

The woman sits down close beside her. "My name is Nina Cavanaugh," she tells Mary. "You look really calm and I'm really scared."

"Mary Orbach," Mary says. "I really don't think there's anything to be scared about. The worst that will happen is some glass will break."

"Really?" Nina Cavanaugh says. Her eyes are wide. "My mom would be very mad at me if I died in a hurricane. In New Jersey, no less."

That makes Mary laugh. "Is New Jersey so bad?"

"It is if you're from Florida. We get enough hurricanes there. You're not supposed to go on a sales trip and run right smack dab into one."

"What do you sell?" Mary asks.

"Medical equipment," Nina Cavanaugh tells her. "I spend a lot of time in doctors' offices and hospitals. Maybe that's why I'm so nervous."

Mary's not sure what the connection is—physicians, injuries, flying glass?—but it doesn't really matter. "I promise you," Mary says to her. "This is nothing. It will pass."

"I'm glad you're so sure," Nina Cavanaugh says.

"Well, I've been here before."

"In a hurricane?"

Mary smiles at Nina. "Not exactly," she says. "Have you ever heard of the Cuban Missile Crisis?"

"Didn't that have something to do with Kennedy?"

"That's right," Mary replies, used to this vagueness from people a generation or so younger than herself. The touchstones of *her* generation—the people and events that seemed unforgettable— are already fading into dim history. They are old stories; they seem more like rumor than reality. She might not even have thought about this particular episode herself if David hadn't mentioned it that afternoon, at Jack's graveside. "The Soviet Union—the Russians—were building nuclear missile bases on Cuba. President Kennedy ordered a naval blockade of the island so the Soviets couldn't bring in any more weapons. Everyone was sure there was going to be a nuclear war. I was in grade school," Mary continues. "And out in Brooklyn, at P.S. 94, the way they dealt with the possibility that nuclear missiles might be exploding any minute was to have drills where they sent us out into the hall—like this—or told us to duck under our desks, cover our heads, and face away from the windows."

"They thought that was going to help?"

"I guess so."

"It sounds pretty dumb," Nina Cavanaugh says.

"It was. But I suppose they didn't know what else to do. I was scared to death," Mary tells Nina—and remembers, in that moment, why she followed her uncle onto the fire escape. He was listening in to the real news; trying to decipher the secret messages, and she wanted to hear them, too. Perhaps he guessed that, and perhaps her motives seemed reasonable to him, because when the window slammed shut, trapping them on the fire escape, he hadn't even reprimanded her. Instead, he had done what must have made sense to him: he had told her to sit down, and then, after taking off his belt, passed it through the belt loop on her corduroy pants and around one of the metal rungs of the fire escape. There was no way, then, that she could carelessly slip through the bars of the fire escape or fall down the ladder, so he must have felt it was safe to leave her while he climbed down the narrow iron stairs between floors, tapping on windows until, a few floors below, a very surprised housewife let him in. Mary felt safe, too—her parents never allowed her on the fire escape, which she understood was a dangerous place—but tied to the metal railing, she was not afraid but, rather, curious. The view of her block from high above was completely new to her; the sky was closer; the breezes, reaching kite strength, pulled her hair.

As soon as David was able to get back into the building, he climbed the interior stairs, unlocked the front door of his apartment, and opened the window. After he untied Mary, he brought her inside and they listened to the short-wave radio, which he had rigged to pick up far-off marine broadcasts. "They see more Soviet ships approaching on their radar," David explained to Mary, helping her to understand what was being said by the faint, garbled voices coming from the radio. He spoke to her gravely, as if she was an adult, not a ten-year-old. "They're going to launch some reconnaissance flights. It looks like the situation could get worse."

"What did they want you to do?" Nina Cavanaugh asks, interrupting Mary's thoughts. "Bend down like this?" Sitting in a cross-legged position, she leans forward and locks her hands behind her head.

"No," Mary tells her. "You were supposed to get on your knees, in a crouch, and bend your head down as far as possible."

Mary turns around to face the wall and gets into the duck-and-cover position. Nina Cavanaugh tries it too. "This really is silly," she says, but now, at least, she's giggling. "People are looking at us."

"You know what?" Mary says, once they've rearranged themselves back into a regular sitting position. "I'm hungry. I saw a sign that said there were vending machines on the next floor, so I'm going to see what they've got. Want to come?"

"I don't know if they'll let us leave," Nina Cavanaugh says, pointing to a pair of men in hotel uniforms who are talking to each other at the end of the hall, blocking access to the elevators.

"They're not the police," Mary says. "And we can take the stairs. Come on," she says, standing up and then offering Nina a hand. "We're already living dangerously."

The two women are off on their mission before the hotel employees even realize they're gone. They find the vending machines and are soon back on their own floor with plenty of snacks. After a while, Mary even returns to her room to get a book, and when she returns, Nina Cavanaugh falls asleep with her head on Mary's shoulder.

A couple of hours later, the hotel intercom announces that the worst of the hurricane has passed, and guests are free to go back into their rooms. After some desultory applause by the people in the hallway, Mary says goodbye to Nina, who pads down the hall to her own room to call her mother and tell her she's survived. In her room, Mary finds that neither the telephone landlines nor her cell phone will work, but she is able to get online with her laptop. Checking the airline schedules, she sees that Newark Liberty Airport has no projection for when it will open, and her flight to Indianapolis, which was supposed to leave this afternoon, is not only canceled, but the airline offers no suggestion about when she might be able to rebook.

She emails the graduate student she is working with to let him know what's going on. With his help, for over a year she has been deeply involved in what has become the most important research project of her life: studying how viruses seem to travel along the old trade routes that date back to the time before Christ. Right now, she is mapping the spread of infection along the Silk Road that stretched from Asia to the Mediterranean. It was a particular cytomegalovirus that beckoned her back to the heart of Byzantium, an organism that was first identified as the cause of diarrheal outbreak in an isolated South Asian ethnic group but is now crossing borders and turning up in neighboring populations, though in a slightly altered form. David was right about viruses; they are strange and canny creatures, kin to the microorganisms that were the original life forms on Earth. Almost every time humans develop a method for defeating them, they find a way to change into a more resistant version of themselves. Presto chango: they are both magical and deadly at the same time.

It was when Mary began to trace the wake of the virus through the pattern of infection it left behind that she realized it was traveling a well-worn path across the mountains and deserts that, for millennia, had perhaps carried more than just salt and silk and spices. Perhaps, she thought, it is not just immigration and airline travel, augmented by all the other aspects of globalization, that are assisting in transmitting facile, ambitious viruses from one faraway place to another—perhaps that is the job of history itself. The World Health Organization and the U.S. Centers for Disease Control are interested in her theories and she has already received a federal grant to support her work.

As soon as she delves into her computer files, she slips off to another place—she is no longer in a hotel on the outskirts of Newark, New Jersey, but in some universe of thought, intensely dark and concentrated but lit by bright threads of possibilities. At some point in the afternoon, as she works, she receives an email from the online travel service she used to book her trip, telling her that flights have resumed and offering a seat on the next plane to Indianapolis. But Mary is comfortable in the hotel and she's busy; she has no classes this week and she doesn't need to be in her office at the university to do her work, so she emails back and asks to be notified about flights tomorrow.

But the next day, Friday, she's still not ready to leave. What is she waiting for? She finally books a seat on a Saturday afternoon flight, but it's actually more expensive than if she had flown out on Friday. So she finally has to admit that the reason she's lingering in New Jersey is that somewhere in the past day or two, she's made the decision that she wants to hear her uncle's lecture. Why not? She has never heard him give a lecture and it is unlikely that she will ever get another chance.

She calls the university, and after they confirm who she is—being a niece means nothing, but a visiting professor does have some clout—they provide her with the information she needs. David, still teaching night school, is giving his lecture at seven p.m.; at six, Mary asks the hotel concierge to get her a cab.

Newark is an old, troubled city—right up there in the top-ten murder capitals of the United States. The university is downtown, sort of hiding in place: with its square, industrial-looking buildings and brick façades it blends right into the urban landscape. But there is greenery beyond the front gate and a quadrangle of sorts, edged with flowery plantings that seem to have weathered the hurricane with minimal damage, though Mary has seen some downed trees and power lines on her ride from the hotel. She finds the lecture hall she's looking for and opens the door to a small auditorium with rows of wooden chairs angled towards a podium that has been placed down front.

It's who's in those seats that Mary finds immediately interesting. To her eye, they appear to be the modern-day descendants of the Silk Road traders: men, mostly, some in turbans and yarmulkes, some Asian, some Arab, some unidentifiable as belonging to one particular ethnic group or another, but all with serious expressions, eyes forward, focused on the spot where the lecturer will appear. These are not casual learners, these night-school students; they are dedicated scholars, earning knowledge by sacrificing time, consuming it in the dinner hour and beyond.

After a few minutes, David walks through a door somewhere in the back of the room and takes his place at the podium. On a blackboard behind him, he writes the title of his lecture — *Nonlinear Stochastic Resonance in Nuclear Fission* — and immediately launches into his talk.

David doesn't seem to notice that Mary is sitting among his students, but that's fine with her; that's not why she's here. In fact, she guesses that he is largely unaware of anyone in the room. It is the ideas with which he is engaged, the thoughts and theories he is expressing that both occupy and illuminate the space within him and around him. He paces back and forth as he speaks, he gesticulates with abandon, he speaks with uncontained excitement. Mary thinks, *If you could look inside his skull right now, his brain would be incandescent. His mind would be burning. It would glow.*

Around her, heads are nodding. Notes are being tapped onto laptops or scribbled on pads of paper as David speaks with increasing urgency: the information he has to share is important and his time is growing short.

Mary understands very little of David's lecture — her field has almost nothing in common with his — but she's happy enough just to sit and listen. Just, for a little while, once again to be near him, in a place that no one else would ever have led her, while he professes his faith that it is possible to explain what might really be going on.

Rerouting the Driver

Like the chauffeur of a car that never stalls
part of my brain plans which way to turn at the next corner,
when to refill the tank,
how to avoid radar, push the limit without a ticket.

She's always ahead of me
testing alternative routes, digesting the meal before I eat.
If I order a vacation, forced retirement
she claims a little work today will help the wheels run smoothly.
If I holler I can drive myself without a body blocking the view
she huffs that someone
must see to business, tinker, think ahead.

Before the next long drive, the next escape into spinning
a new project, the next detour from recollection,
I'll sugar that chauffeur's tank.
The wheels, always going nowhere, really won't.

Look at the light change. Red to green.
Her eyes blink, their color restored.
Seized pistons have fractured her glare at the endless road.
She leaves the machine, its door hung open to rust in the rain.
Look inside the crossroads café:
I'm done with leftovers among bright tablecloths;
she's drinking a steamy cup, present.

Atlas for Returning

I will marry this forsaken summer
              with my wheels, veiled in sweat
rich as beads strung
              down my back & thighs, uxorious
bride to night's sulphur
              quilled with firebugs & reflected
highway signs & crickets
              rubbing music from their bodies like a saw.
I will lose my heart to each part of her
              scored & sapping, muscled with dirt.
I tear through states like finish-line tape
              while the afternoon sends heat
lightning, rain rigged from theater wings,
              flown in for one act, sailed deftly back out.
Roseate spoonbills persist south & the flat rivers muddy
              with alligators thawed brutal, reptile hearts slowed
to beat once every four minutes.
              If I stop now fear
                     will make a warren of me,
              all dug out.
Will you take me back
              to that flank of western sky
I once swam not knowing
              I could drown? The water here: broad-
shouldered & caulked with prayer
              so old it dragged a thousand years
through pawpaw & sumpweed
              before sugarcane got sworn in.
Will you take me back knowing
              I carry where I have been the way
a crayfish bears both her claws & eggs
              globed to swimmerets like pearl?
I never learned where here is,
              only the silence for *deep*
when fingers beg *plough*.

Of Crawdads and Bats

I knew how to catch a crawdad when I was five,
        but I've forgotten.
I knew the way a gravel drive could be tossed
                piece by piece into the sky
        to draw down bats at twilight.

Rain called the crawdads from the earth
        the night that my bare feet dodged
                their dens, dirt volcanoes, and plodded
        to the forest's edge. I conjured insects
of pebbles, launched one at a time, baiting
        all that flew in the canopy.

        A black streak.

With a fishing net, I pinned
                the diving bat to the wet grass, knelt
        and felt him through the blue mesh.
My fingers touched his belly, the soft fur
                so like my kitten's ear, his wings
        the delicate rubber of her padded paws,
                his little hands like crawdad feet
    atop my own.

        I was muddy. Quiet, and invincible.
        I was never afraid,
                not of fangs or claws or darkness, then.

On the Clutter of My Office

I've outgrown my shell again, a hermit
crab hoarding spiral memories. Corkboard
poorly grasps the past, tacks piercing
what will never stay in place. It slips
away, this vision of fresh love as fine
sand, secure in the lines of my upturned hands.
A waterpark receipt, flattened penny, the desiccated
corpse of a rose — these grains overflow, pinned
to the walls and strewn on shelves.

Were I to trap these grains in pinched
glass, they may capture time in truthful ways — bottle up
one honest hour. Fallen behind my desk,
a bowling scorecard. You broke two hundred.
Penciled hearts orbit your name — did I sit on your lap
between frames? Did you slip a thirsty
hand across my thigh? Saltwater defines
our planet. Life ends in thirst's absence.
The scorecard flutters to the floor.

During neap tide, the sun and moon wrench
our Earth with equal force, seeking
the perfect balance between high and low.
It's the least human time. I've forgotten what it is
I want — a tidal wave, a drink, a shell. Awash
at sea, I lift my fingers. Wave. I know that
you are standing there, beyond my office door,
but salt and sand obscure my vision.

Transfer Station

There is a place for everything.
Divided neatly, all the bins
are labeled, one for anything
you'd think of. And a man to ask
when you're not sure. "If it can tear,"
is what the dump attendant says
about what paper is allowed.
He'll also clarify that "dump"
is not what we should call this place
from which all leavings are removed
to distant, dumpish parts unnamed
and scarcely known. It's all *transferred*.
All swept away. Except, of course,
for items left in the single-wide
identified as the "Swop Shoppe."
We're Yankees, still beholden to
the old proverbs and promises
to *use it up, to wear it out,*
to make it do or do without.
So here we leave what can't be trash,
the artifacts for which no bins
exist: old corporate coffee mugs,
cassette tapes, china, blenders, books,
and plastic-corded telephones;
small furniture and Scrabble boards,
red-eyed alarm clocks, pots and pans.
And from these shelves and tables take
for free whatever things we want
to bring to useful life again.
Our waffle iron, hand-mixer,
the extra wine glasses, the pot
we plant with flowers every year —
all came from here. I don't recall
what all we've left behind in trade.
I guess this is a transfer, too —
from someone else's life to this

waystation at the edge of town
and then at last to us, to ours,
this pot I fill with snapdragons,
this glass from which I drink my wine.

Ashley Inguanta, photograph

Terminal

Where your trains are scheduled to connect

but you step down to the platform
to discover they're standing
at opposite ends of the station.

A sudden flash forward to derailment
marks the precise moment you come

to the awareness you're going to die.

X-rays hanging
like undergarments on the light box,

and depending on whether the car needs
an oil change or the nib's dried out
on the uncapped pen or

the kitchen uses bacon grease
for the pancake griddle,

you will variously describe the tumors
as a cascade

of orchids, an entanglement
of butterflies, sausages
like drapes in a butcher shop window.

Those cleaving multiples —
suspicious,

like a single cloud is suspicious
chugging
through a sunny day.

You think of yourself as seed,
then blister on the surface,
then an entire field sown,

the combine
rumbling toward harvest, and you run

through the alphabet (twice), but still

can't remember the name
of the neighbor, bent over
her porch pots with bucket and snips,

trimming back the excess blooms.

Not one intact pencil
in the junk drawer for constructing
your reliable checklist.

It occurs to you
there should always be two caskets.

Like boxcars—

one for the trundle in,
one for the slog out.

What They Missed in the Obituary

Won't be a cakewalk,
what he always said.

Preferred handkerchiefs with lace,
macaroons to pralines.
Took his beverages *adulterated*.

How his thick-socked heels hung over
the ends of his sandals when he walked.

Saw court twice. Won once.

Only Providence I know
is the one in Rhode Island.

Irresistible were lemon bars,
the scent of matchheads,
that tender place at the back of a knee.

Chased down a tumbleweed on 395.
Took off the door to fit it in the car.

All he could muster
to say about the mustang:
Lovely horse. Just couldn't cure his feet.

Beautiful was a space capsule, returning
from orbit. False eyelashes on a woman
whose name he'd never know.

Darn fool waste of a plane,
he said of Air Force One.

"Abandon the Absurd"
read the sign in his yard.
Abandon crossed out, replaced with Embrace.

Certain words repeated
for the very sound of them: *bilious,*
undercover, regeneration.

That long-ago hairpin.
How he still could feel the girl's silky braid.

One letter separates a fellow from fallow.

That the goings-on in Babel
made more sense than not.
He's a mean one, your God.

Kept every penny he found in the street.

Could paint around a window
and never brush the glass.

Cotton on the wind
really makes you stop and think.

Thought tunnel vision underrated.

Said he wanted to percolate like coffee
back into the earth.

You won't find any heroes in the headlines.

Treating the Chickens for Mites on the Back Porch

When the silked undersides
of feathers become a forest
of small amber teardrop-creatures, I bring
the chickens to the porch. I wear a ripped sweatshirt,
fill the lit ghosts of trash bags
with industrial pesticide strong enough
to kill a cat, but not
the birds with reptilian legs, birds primitive,
their beaks spearlike. The industrial pesticide is flour-soft
and almost innocent when the porch lamp catches it.
The bags swallow the chickens one after another. Their heads
on the outside, they stand still, eyes dark
with sleep. I shake the dust
into their feathers like dry rain. They step
into the henhouse, peppered with neurotoxic snow. They settle.

In the morning you are still gone and the sun
is pouring over a shattered glass of dew. The chickens
step scale-footed outside,
stand blank in the face of dawn.

Theology of the Body

If your body   mine   so alike
      in the half-light   suspend between them
      an act *of grave depravity*

then why is it the name of the heavenly father   not my name
you have said in a ragged whisper
              the single syllable hard-edged
    clawing from the hollow   of your throat

        ✿

    You were not born   in the grasp
      of catechism   did not feel the echo of
        This inclination   *constitutes for most of them a trial*

    in the window's white light   your eyes opened
      to the blank faces   of walls
        as you called without longing   that name

Devon Browning, *Getting Past My Bullshit*, oil on linen, 30" x 40"

The Love of God

At the Holy Family Retreat for Roman Catholic Teens, in the chapel lit with accidentally sexy red candles, we are asked to revisit our latest mistakes and ask Him if He can find it in His Sacred Heart of hearts to forgive us.

Forgive me, Lord, for my poor judgment in consenting to attend this cornball retreat. I was led astray by my friend, Jess, and her ever-lethal good intentions. I know that's no excuse, but believe me, my blunder has been its own punishment. There is nothing else that You can possibly do to me.

Here at the retreat, we sleep two to a room in the nunnery dormitories. As you would expect, the twin beds are very narrow. There is no air-conditioning. It is June in the convent somewhere in the middle of the woods and already hot as hell, which in my mind isn't giving us much incentive to behave like angels.

This morning, Peggy, the chief nun, woke us by banging pots together in the kitchen—a much more dulcet sound than her screechy and—even worse—earnest coloratura:

Holy, holy,
ho-oh-ly Lord!
God of power, God of light!
Heaven and earth are filled with
yore glor-ee.
Ho-SAH-na, in the high-EST!
Ho-SAH-na!
HO-SAH-NUH in the high…
EeEeEeEeEeEeEe-EST!

The noise was violent and tremendous, like Earth being made. But no. Just breakfast. Somehow Jess managed to sleep through the whole goddamn thing. On the Third Day, She overslept. She was pissed that I didn't wake her, but she knows like I know from years of sleepovers how impossible she is to wake. Her hair rippled and tangled across the pillow in a way that she could not have planned. Her open mouth, buried in her hair, drooling in it, her hair spread across her pillow like light. I couldn't possibly wake her.

"You sleep like a dead person," I told her in the afternoon. "She is risen!"

"Is this how it's going to be in the fall? Are you going to let me sleep through my college exams and stuff?"

"Exams, yes. Stuff, no."

"I mean it. Can I count on you to wake me in the future?"

"Sista, iamb yore roommate knot chore keeper."

"You at least could have tried."

"How do you know I didn't?"

Jess was fined one bracelet for her tardiness. We receive colored bracelets for random acts of kindness performed within eyeshot of nuns and chaperones. Whoever collects the most WWJD bands receives some kind of Christ-themed grand prize, which, like Jesus, is necessarily shrouded in mystery. I'm not sure that the nuns realize how old we are. We are to record each good deed in the black composition books distributed at the beginning of the retreat. On the blank line on the cover of hers, Jess has printed her name, and on mine I have written, "Holy Shit." I have sixteen bracelets, and now Jess has three.

I've had a few close calls. Whenever Peggy says, "God is good!" we are expected to rejoin in chorus, "All the time!" When she says, "All the time!" we are to respond, "God is good!" Very early in the morning. I only move my lips along with the others because I don't want to risk reprising embarrassing slipups such as "God is time!" and "All is good!" It's like she's *trying* to confuse us. It's like how at Mass they changed the words of the response from "And also with you" to "And with your spirit" to see who was really paying attention.

We are encouraged/required to wear the bracelets for the duration of our week-long stay at the nunnery: wearing not on but *over* our sleeves the tacky, neon, twisted, dirty, fraying friendship bracelets that represent the contents of our hearts so that they may be subjected to the loving scrutiny of our brothers and sisters.

Despite or because of all of those loving stares, morning Mass does not put Jess in a forgiving mood. At recreation hour, she ditches me to play dusty Chinese checkers with a klatsch of true believers. The rec room is a deconsecrated chapel furnished with mismatched couches that were probably never intended to be orange. In their faded state, they almost look like they could match. I wander to the retired organ in the corner. I would sit down and play it, were it not conspicuous as well as likely verboten.

On the organ bench leans an unplugged karaoke machine.
It's old with a big-ass boombox attached and it takes cassette
tapes. I guide the plug to an outlet behind the organ, and I rewind,
searching for a song I know.

I may not be able to hit the high notes, but to compensate
I sing "Killing Me Softly" with as much latent sexuality as I can
summon at such short notice. I dedicate it to Jess because she is
pretending not to know me. Jess's face flushes, but the archdiocese
in-residence actually loves it. The bug-eyed, fuzzy-sweatered priest
responsible for today's homily on purity takes me aside for a private conversation with my breasts about how my Gift of Music can
be used to Glorify the Lord. I honestly can't tell if he's perverted or
just short. Two more bracelets for me: one from Fuzzy Sweater and
one from Peggy because these people clearly don't communicate.

Take that, Jess.

I'm not even the one who wants this.

❋ ❋ ❋

After lunch, the nuns lead us through the herb garden and
into the woods and ask us each to pick out a rock. They are obviously running out of things to do with us. We return to the nunnery with rocks. We form a circle. Holding rocks, we conduct a
group discussion about how Jesus is our Rock. A guest speaker,
the guitarist with a self-destructive-looking buzz-cut who plays
at our Masses, talks about his struggle with cocaine and miscella-
neous addictions and how Jesus is also now his Rock. He is holding a magenta geode. He keeps looking at his shoes like a bad kid,
hiding under the ghost of his former long hair. He is inarticulate
in the way that you are when you are being nothing but honest.
He shares more details about his addiction than the nuns probably
commissioned—but as he talks, that stupid rock keeps catching the
fluorescent light and honest-to-goodness glistering.

"It was like everything was singing to me, you know what I
mean," he says to his shoes, "but then I got over it." He must miss
it something terrible.

More than anything, my rock looks like a potato. If I had
known the point of this exercise in advance, I would have selected
a small smooth one like everyone else. A worry stone. A pocket
rock. A skipping stone.

On the rock that rests in Jess's fist, there is a white ladybug that is as compact and perfect as a pearl earring stud. It matches the whitehead at the corner of her nose. She does not see the ladybug. I touch her shoulder lightly and whisper to her to look. Jess, being Jess, shrieks. She shakes and beats at her rock, which is less efficient than dropping it but is also more cinematic. Punitive action is once again taken against her jewelry.

"I thought it was a maggot," she whispers.

"It had wings."

Jess shudders. "I know."

❊ ❊ ❊

We are excused to return to our rooms to change for the evening service.

I can tell right away that Jess has another one of her migraines. She's making that face like she's anxious about what her eyebrows are up to. Without saying a word, she sits on the floor in front of my cot. I sit down on the edge and bend forward to rub her neck. Where her spine meets her nape—that works every time. She makes pained noises and nudges her back against my hands.

"I think the nuns stole my panties," she huffs.

"What?"

"The ones from yesterday! I can't find them!"

"They're over there on the lampshade. How the hell did you manage that?"

"I was in a bit of a hurry this morning."

"You're still mad about that?"

"It's just that it bothers me," she said, "that you don't seem to be taking this retreat all that seriously."

"Hell no!"

"Val!"

"I'm sorry. I'm uncomfortable."

"You didn't have to come."

"I came because you asked me to."

"I needed this, to do this with you. Don't you get that?"

"That wasn't a question. How am I supposed to answer it?"

"I need this. I'm not you. I'm not—"

"Not what?"

"Not, like . . . laminated."

"What?"

I do know what she means, though. She thinks I'm impervious—which hurts.

"Oh, for the love of God," I say, and Jess says, "Fine, Val. You turn this into a word game and you are always going to win. Is that what you want?"

One of Jess's nostrils is bigger than the other. It gives her face drama, constant conflict. She's self-conscious about that, but me, I love it. Her face is so like her. How often does a person like that happen? I say, "That's not what I want."

❊   ❊   ❊

Jess and I met at religious education in middle school. Her mother taught our class; her mother's hated me From The Beginning. They were serving us a snack in the gymnasium, bowls of stale pretzels and plastic medicine cups of pop. I was downing Diet Cokes like shots and pretending not to notice Jess's long pale disapproving face looming over my shoulder. I could see it reflected in the waxed gym floor. I remember thinking, "Now that is a girl who is self-destructively conscientious."

Jess was never one to waste time on friendly greetings. Within seconds, she was in my face like *60 Minutes*: "Did you know that drinking Coke is worse for your teeth than drinking battery acid?"

"Does battery acid come in Diet?"

She blushed. "I read that on a Snapple lid. A regular Snapple."

She looked healthier when she blushed, though also sadder. She was inclined to fear, faith, migraines, and outbursts. They were always melodramatic but she didn't know that—because she meant them. They made me laugh, but they also made me never want to stop watching her.

My face is ruddy, so even if I blushed, no one would ever be able to tell, but I was mortified that night at religious education when I was asked to recite the Apostles' Creed by myself and I pronounced it Pon-tea-is Pilot. "What I envy about you," Jess said to me, "is how you don't care."

❊   ❊   ❊

Standing in the chapel tonight, even I have to admit that it is a Moment: those red candles, the epiphanic scent of polished silver, the sound of dripping wax and muted music, the licking of acoustic guitars and the repeated lines, like a mantra, "Holy spirit, come into our li-ives. Holy spirit, make us truly wi-ise." Amazing the cheesy sentiments you can get away with when you accompany them with beautiful music—and Jess is on her knees, literally on her knees, weeping, weeping real tears. Everyone asks me what's wrong with her. Everyone somehow knows to ask me. "I don't know," I say. "I don't know."

Fuzzy Sweater gets down on Jess's level. Even he thinks that her penitence is excessive. "My child, what could you possibly have to be so guilty about?"

Jess's voice sounds underwater. Her eyeliner is smeared. "I've done some really bad things."

Fuzzy Sweater frowns, and I can see that he, at least, knows exactly how old we are. He is positive that he can see where this is going.

❀ ❀ ❀

Jess collects men named after the Books of the Bible. She's already had John, Luke, Ezra, Joshua, Daniel, Obadiah, Mark, and a duplicate Mark. Me: I opt to put my mouth all over a guy with a name like a progressive verb. Darren, Collin, Ryan, and Ryan again: the stages of courtship.

I was only kidding about Obadiah.

We all hate when Jess has a boyfriend. It means we never get to see her, and when we do, the boy is there and she's acting like such an airhead, it doesn't count as Jess being there. She develops a prissy almost-accent and a delicate appetite.

Jess blames me for scaring away the original Mark. She had asked him to finish her salad at prom because she was feeling peaked. "Yesterday," I said, "Jess called me to tell me that she just ate nine Tagalongs. She called me for that express purpose."

"Don't *tell* people that."

"Who's people?"

❀ ❀ ❀

Ryan and I haven't decided yet if we're going to break up this summer or try long distance, but Jess and I will be at Minnesota, and he'll be all the way over at State. I wanted to meet new people. Jess was the one who practically begged me to be her college roommate. She said that she had forgiven me for both Marks.

Jess skipped Senior Skip Day to see a movie with the Second Coming of Mark. The rest of us were barbecuing and drinking together on the beach at the park and pushing each other into the disgusting water. It was one of the last times we were going to be able to be together.

I supposed that our friends could feel it too—the way Jess has of being conspicuously not there, to the extent that her absence becomes a presence that overshadows everything else. Like God, I guess, for unhappy atheists.

Liz was the one who suggested that we leave the barbecue to go after Jess; Brit was the one who drove. Liz bent back the passenger seat of the two-door sedan so that I could stumble into the back. From this isolated seat, I offered snarky commentary so that they would not forget to talk to me.

Brit, who worked at the movies, bribed her coworker with a coveted Saturday night shift to persuade her to show us the security footage of Theater 11. Jess and Mark 2.0 were the only two people in the theater. They were holding hands, not making out, and not even holding hands in a cute way—more of a "whoops, I rested my hand on the cup-holder but yours happened to be there already" way.

Stacy, the coworker, was overweight and middle-aged and single and pimpled like a teenager and enjoying this as much as Liz and Brit were. "Want to see another camera angle?"

"Do you perverts always sit at the concierge desk and watch people watch movies?" I said.

"Except when we catch couples making out. Then we're supposed to go in there and break it up, if necessary."

"Interesting."

Liz smacked me and giggled, "You're bad!"

"What constitutes necessary?"

"We never actually, like, do it," said Brit.

"Theater 11 will be to your left and down the hall," said Stacy, pointing. She winked. "Enjoy your show."

"You too," said Liz, then she giggled. "Whoops!"

We wore tubs of popcorn as tophats and crawled between the rows of seats so that only our disguises were visible from above.

I was not wearing capri pants like the others and my hands and knees got sticky.

On the screen, Cameron Diaz and Ashton Kutcher's heads and shoulders appeared to be having passionate sex. The shaggy back of Ashton's hair was bobbing in ecstasy, and Cameron's bra straps were falling down her forearms, the cast-off elastic looking sort of lost. The shot was always cropped based on her nipples, always cut off right above them. Her mouth made suggestive shapes.

When they saw us, Mark 2.0 laughed and chucked Peanut M&Ms at our faces, and Jess began to scream. Her seat rolled up with a thud as she ran at me.

"Stop following me! You're scaring me!"

Liz and Brit looked alarmed. I never got blamed for anything.

"Hey, hey," said Liz. "If you're going to be mad at anyone, you should be mad at me."

"It wasn't even Val's idea."

"The popcorn tubs were."

"Okay, except for the popcorn. That was totally Val."

"Stop following me!" Jess screamed at me, stomping past our friends. I uncrossed my arms and she lunged into them, crying. "Stop," she murmured, "it's scary."

The others were more surprised by my reaction than by hers. They would expect this kind of thing from Jess, but they were surprised to see me hug her without making fun. My hair smelled like charred hamburger and my wet bikini had soaked through my t-shirt. When I let go of Jess, she tripped forward a little. On her shirt, there was a wet mark that matched mine under her breast-bone—because she's so tall.

"Jess." Brit broke into shrill, nervy giggles. "You look like you have two sets of boobs, Jess."

Distractedly, Jess whined, "I don't! You guys!"

"What did you think I said?" Brit repeated herself and Jess cried, "Oh!" Then she stopped crying and started cry-laughing. All was forgiven. Once again. For the moment. As always.

This was not the first time that Jess had told me to stop, nor would it be the last. In sophomore English class, when we had to write character sketches of our neighbors, I may have mentioned how when she laughs, she looks like she is standing against the current of a warm summer wind: how her asymmetrical little nose flattens against her face and she throws her head back as though she wants to feel your joke running through her hair. I was the one who told her that Jordan was cheating on her. I let it slip to Landon that her father had performed a background check on him because he was black. This is what I do; I tell other people's truths.

At her graduation party, I screamed and screamed at the DJ, "Play 'Alejandro'! Alejandro, Alejandro!" until he glared and listened. Marching in rhythm with that bouncily militant dance beat, all of our friends and classmates came running down the hill into the temporary backyard dance floor. They were cheering and waving their drinks over their heads and chanting, "I know that we are young and I know that you may love me, but I just can't be with you like this anymore…Alejandro!" Jess wouldn't speak to me for weeks, though—like I told her—to everyone else, it was nothing but another perfect song to which one could freak.

"People are going to think something happened between us," was her argument, and mine was, "Something did." Drunk at prom, we had ditched the dance and her prick of a date and my parents who were chaperoning, and in their empty house, she kissed me, letting me pull gently on her hoop earring, stretching her earlobe. I said, "That was something."

At graduation, because my name came after hers in the alphabet, I walked across the stage behind her. "I'm following you," I whispered, as we shook our way through the procession of important hands, and she told me that wasn't funny.

She was right. It wasn't. It was cruel of me. Redundant. I have been following Jess since before we met, and I'll be following her for long after the fights that we will have in college, in which we will scream awful, accurate things at each other. I have always been, and will always be, what Jess is afraid to see when she looks over her shoulder. The two of us, so young and gay, as they say.

✻ ✻ ✻

According to Fuzzy Sweater, all of us have our gifts. I guess drama is Jess's, and mine is advanced evasive maneuvering—and who better to understand God-given gifts than the Genius who believed that they were such a good idea in the first place.

By the end of the retreat week, I will be wearing a nickel rosary around my neck, because I had the most bracelets. Jess would break out if she wore it because, even if she had won, she's allergic. It's an injustice, really. You can't be good all the time; no one sees everything, and Jess is unlucky. Unlike her, I have excellent instincts for when I'm being watched, which is probably the reason why she believes in God and I do not.

In our cell after the chapel service, I hook contraband headphones into the stolen big-ass boombox from the rec room to listen again and again to the song that they were playing. It's stuck in my head, and I can't get it out.

"I can hear you listening to that song over and over again."

I start and pull the sheets over me. I thought that Jess was asleep.

"You can hear me listening?"

She sighs loudly enough for me to hear.

"Shut up," I say, "I'm trying to pray."

Jess sighs again. Under the covers, I am writing in the composition book of Holy Shit:

Dear God, Please forgive me for loving her best when she is on the verge of unraveling. When she is miserable, I will keep her misery company. I shall be the flesh that she wraps around her bones, but I will let in a draft so that she shivers and pulls me tight about her. The Father, the Son, and all the other holy men, who, based on what I have heard about them, have no blessed clue what I mean and would not approve, amen.

Jesus. God. I know it's hokey, but I'm trying. Don't laugh at me.

I can tell that Jess is not asleep, only pretending. "Val?" she whispers.

I roll over and close my eyes and we are back in the chapel with the glow of the red candles making us blush and blush, except for Jess, who is kneeling and shadowed. My foot has fallen asleep on the kneeler. When I try to stand, it is so numb I can't feel the floor. I fall on my face. Jess takes my arm, and I stumble out of our pew with her, laughing with pain as the feeling returns, and I am ashamed not because I believe in any of this shit but because I couldn't even give her that one moment, this one week, this one thing. The retreat frowns on makeup and Jess has cried off the little that she was wearing. In the glow of the candles, her face is nude, lunar. Her arms are bare. I could never do what she can, not in a week, not in a million years. What must it be like to believe in someone who will love you no matter what?

"I'm —" I start to say.

"You're what?" Her tone sounds tender because, in this sacred context, she must whisper.

I don't say sorry; I say nothing. I say it out loud: "Nothing." As long as she has to keep forgiving me, she can't forget me—and I couldn't do that to her. In the beginning, when He was in such a giving mood, I don't think the creator planned on people like me who are always going to be sorry.

Ashley Inguanta, photograph

Standing in the James River

Water laps my waist,
minnows greet me with kisses.

They test my fingers for food, taste
each flake of my shallow palms

flick my thumbs, scales
washing my feet   shins   thighs.

Water cools day, humidity my flesh
sweat bulbs on the underside

of my upturned forearms. They emerge as islands
to face light for the first time in months.

I am mobile in breath.
Transparent stained-glass

welcoming the flock with arms half-bent
soft cup hands   heaven-seeking eyes.

I was nine when Amanda baptized me
in her own name, confirmed me as her friend forever.

My only baptism. My only summer with her. She netted
her fingers above my ponytail, tingled my skull, spread

warmth down my neck into my wet hands, over my toes in the muck.
Ready? Her calm smile. Her pink bikini.

Our soft growing breasts inches from each other.
She pinched my nose, dunked me

full beneath goose-loved water, no time to close my eyes
sky white through the ripple, I thought

I will drown iwilldrowniwill — until she lifted me.

A dragonfly studies me with
purple eyes, a mountain

concealing her mate.
She meets my other arm

balancing on fine hair above skin.
Her sky-tipped tail

bobs in the crook of my elbow
a needle calls a vein.

she braces wings of cellophane
in downstream gusts. So easy.

Off for mosquitos she flies,
gone as every summer-camp girl.

With the water at my ribs
I rest. With creeks of sweat

through hills of tense muscle
and shoulder-blade valleys

I rest. Patient for each fish to fill
and vanish my portrait.

Never so still.
Never my heart so aflame.

Echo

Come when you are called, or else you will produce an echo. You didn't know you were in that sleep, even as you dreamed someone was calling, and were you that someone? Come when you are called, or else you will produce an echo. On a concrete floor near a wall that blooms with a hole: a ceramic black tailfin like a whale's, a fluke curved like a pause, and within it a hollow space enough for a small hand to fit up to the wrist and wear it cradled like a cast or outstretched like a glazed glove. A hollow space enough, or sometimes, like a joke or a mouth to feed, both too little and too much.

Sometimes, like a joke, you might be difficult to remember and not come when you are called. In this way an echo makes from an absence a repetition; from a call, its response. Were you being called? Were you an echo, a dream, a mouth to feed, a joke? A fluke, a pause, a cast, a glove, a small hand, a hollow space. A wall, an absence, a repetition, a response, a sleep: a someone. Come when you are called, or else you will produce an echo. By a call, you might be woken from a sleep you didn't even know you were an echo in. You didn't even know you were an echo in.

Reflections

They need our help, these mirror folk
flopping from their frames the moment
we turn off the lights. They try so hard,
bouncing against dark windows, not sure
which side to part their hair.

Where does yours go at night?

Buttons askew, it wanders the polished halls
of your elementary school, slips behind
your childhood desk, and sits with folded hands.
Stretching tall and twice as thin, it tries to read
books made of palindromes.

In the dark it resembles you.

Simulcast

I am my stepfather's son: I am an old woman.
Shadows darken his hospital room where,
in his dementia, he imagines
I am the child who died
before my birth. The difference—
nine months. Time enough for me to fly
cross-country, one womb to another,
and grow into the Air Force pilot my stepfather sees
when he looks at me.

Supposing I told my mother:
I'm me, but not me. I think she'd carry on
painting her paintings, knowing
nothing real is solid, but formed
from semi-transparent glazes,
each layer revealing
the layer below. How else to explain why
when she brought home this new father,
I recognized his voice, clung to his stories
with dizzy adoration? Love

is energy. Energy can't be destroyed,
only passed along—a secret
whispered ear to ear. Look
how his television plays a thousand shows
simultaneously. Look
how his fingers reach
to find the channels—

Slugs

Every day they quadruplefy. My mother
finds them eating her Dorothy Benedict hostas,
which have puckered blue leaves and cost $200
at the horticultural fair, so she shoots them
with squirts of ammonia fired from a plastic pistol.
They're always copulating —
switching their sexes to and fro, peppering the mulch
with infinitesimal eggs. My stepfather draws a graph
to show the rise and fall of slug empires
concealed in the moist bed by the pool,
slithery gray brains burrowed beneath the weight
of Persian carpets. Years and years of secrets.
I should confess: I've left my teaching job,
driven away a decent husband, and pursued a romance
with a woman. Mother comes in from the garden,
limping from the want of new knees,
sits beside my stepfather, and ponders his ragged rows
of numbers. If I wait long enough, they'll die
and I won't have to tell.

Kissing After Illness

Our lips are so slow. They meet cell
by cell, as though they've traveled vast
distances like pilgrims, bent under
their tin pots and blankets. Our lips
arrive, but even when they touch,
they wait. The way a midwife enters
the room of a laboring woman and says
nothing, does nothing. Just watches, joining
the river of the woman's breath.
So our lips wait. But not exactly wait.
Nor exactly rest. But press, suspended
in a stillness that is the marrow
of kissing. The stem-cell of kissing.
A laden, blood-filled lull. Our lips
are not eager, not glad. They are almost
free of intention. There is only
a brush against inquisitive
nerves. Our lips mate like I once
watched the mindless bodies
of leopard slugs slide over and under,
infinitely slow in their voluptuous entwining.
Strange. And strangely beautiful, how their long
shining translucent penises, fluted and frilled,
unfurl from their heads, swirling, knotting
around each other. Then blossom, swell
into a flower. It takes hours. And our lips
stunned into stupor, our tongues
still sleeping, hot, mute,
in no hurry to be born.

Body

I never ride the bus without a book, some purpose
to my waiting between here and there, a way
to fill the time with things more important
than the journey. And yet I am distracted, always,

by the cacophony the bus presents, the conversations
I am allowed to watch and hear: the queer kids
talking about threesomes, the punky andro-
butchy girl sitting on the lap of the femme-y

hipster boy, talking as if the rest of us aren't there, loud,
about her sex with women not him, which girl is hot,
who gets to watch, if he'll be allowed to touch
or not, interrupting my reading of whatever book

or magazine I had that day, forgotten as I wonder
if all that's coming from her loud gravelly voice
isn't a performance as much as her double-sided lip-
piercings, her blue and black bihawk, the chunky

way everything hangs on her solid frame. Listening
to them, I don't feel young anymore. I know
it's frivolous to say I'm old. I am nowhere near
the grinding down of my body past any point

recognizable, the body finished. When Joe died,
I was wrecked. The way his body kept
moving, the forced gasp of a bellows inside his chest,
his breath the last thing to let go of him, the body

trained for its work even after the vent shut off.
The nurse said it could take hours. We left.
What else could we do? Listen to that noise
until it extinguished? So we left him there,

and I was grandfatherless. He and Grammie
should have gone together, holding hands,
their breaths slowing easy. He waited too long.
After the cremation I cleaned their house,

the hoarded morphine, the right-to-die
literature packing their file cabinets. He had missed
the window of opportunity. The time you get
to decide. Watching Grammie go alone: years,

it took her, asking where Joe was, then asking
what his name had been, then just waiting in pain
for everyone to leave her alone. When we said goodbye
all that was left was her rattling breath, gurgling

from her wrinkled throat like a coffee-maker. I couldn't
shake the simile in my head, so I said it, and we started
laughing, snot and tears and laughter at the sound
of mornings, the suck and release of a snore

with water running through it. I wanted to read to her
poems of dying, peace, love—but I couldn't
speak, so I read to myself. Weren't they really for me
anyway? Everyone wants some solace, someplace.

I say everyone as if having a body is always
so easy. As if the body can't be transformed.
I spend hours reveling in the reshaping
of other bodies: *RuPaul's Drag Race*, how much I love

the sparkle, the shine, to judge each queenliness.
How well they pass. How much interest for passing.
How at another poetry reading, *important* and *significant*,
we were crowded into the back room of the bar, sparkling

lights on the stage, genderqueer and transfolks reading
about how they are more than their bodies. Be honest—
I was thinking about their bodies, what choices were made,
how much T, transition, and time went into crafting

this body or that. And how white. And how strongly
I reacted—that shade of privilege
doesn't suit you, hunty—
to every transman's word about a woman's body,

when one poet read about rescuing Gretel and I thought,
Motherfucker, don't you know that little girl was the one
who pushed the witch into the fire?
Who wants all that masculinity, I wonder? My wife

will strap on a dick beneath boxers, wear a blazer,
bring flowers when she picks me up for a date, lift me
into bed when I call her handsome, handsome. I never said
I was a logical person. Why else would I love poetry?

Why else define my body's slide against the body
of another woman, joy loud as the queer kids on the bus?
Pushing their bodies brash into my shoulder
as they exit, while I go back to my magazine, wondering

why the "inspiring" photographs of artsy writer's magazines
are always black-and-white. Grayscale makes up the bodies
of brown women on display—strange, exotic, unique
as whatever they are selling. Two young girls balance

one atop the other, head to head, flat sequins shining
against their leotards. Children practicing their act,
the little one probably not even dizzy anymore.
The base girl, older, has eyes that focus somewhere off,

ignoring the camera that captures their moment.
Behind them, the edge of the circus tent, ground,
as they hold their arms balanced like mirrors,
round heads connected by a cushion of hair.

Pages later, another photograph: a woman,
her hair covered entirely by iguanas, a crown
of the living lizards, many gazes asking, asking—
I can't know what that spiky crowd is thinking.

Maybe it is market day. Maybe it is a celebration.
Maybe she knows the turistas love a good show. She looks
directly at the camera; it is the iguanas who look away
and out. I am tired of reading.

I put down the magazine, look out
the window. A mother climbs onto the bus, settles down
with her newborn. She chats with the man
across the aisle. The baby is three weeks, the baby

is a girl baby, the baby's head will not stay wrapped
in the swaddle tight to her mother. *Oh yeah, she nosey,
she so nosey, always want to see what's goin' on.* She wants to be
another body in the world, in the world, another body.

Devon Browning, *My Hair*, oil on linen, 30" x 40"

She looked as though her hands would never
hold a shotgun to her own head
as she heard the music of her children's
laughter — or maybe it was the din
of her baby's crying — after she sent
the older ones outside to play. Out, out.
She sent them out of the house.

How did she do it with a shotgun?
Perhaps her toes were agile, like mine,
feet like hands, one dexterous toe
against the trigger. Or did she pull
the trigger at all? Did anyone wonder?

On Secrets

1

"Tell me a gossip," my friend says
in her slight French accent, patting
a burgundy stain onto her lips. I tell her.

2

The dusty turtle inches forward on the rock, teeters
on the edge of it, then flings itself
into the brown river water. It surfaces,
shell shining black now, then disappears
into the churn: I won't see it again.

3

A secret requires tending, like a toddler
or a wound. Do not leave a secret alone
or it will write itself all over the walls,
the one word it knows, over and over,
scratched into the furniture. It will hurt
itself. Don't poke at it either, stop that, you'll make it worse.

4

The tree raises its ruffle of reddening buds,
sun-swollen and sore — cut back
from the live wire, limbs twist,
splayed and bark-gnarled,
naked. The body
displays its history, it can't help that.

5

Enough of him died that he can no longer speak.
He peers, his brown eyes narrow, he moves
the arm he can move. "Yes,"

his mother says, and holds the straw to his lips.
"You like that, I know." And she does.

6

You can cover a secret if you must,
story sewn on story like a quilt, warm
and stiff with stitching until it's washed.

Or smooth it over, wear away
each identifying ridge, wave by wave,
until it is round and hard and pleasing
as the stone you rub between finger and thumb.

Better to hide it? To seal it
behind walls where it gnaws
and scrabbles at the plaster all night?
You could do that.

If you plant it in the lawn, expect a seedling.
A secret is hardy and will grow almost anywhere.

7

The intimacy of dissection, clever knife
parting the fascia. Today
we bury the body, having been known
down to bone's slick surface.
What did we miss?

Potter's Field

This ground was reserved for something useful once,
grocery store or schoolhouse, the proposed location
of a cinema, amusement park. But not for long.
Even today Hitler's bunker is simply a car park
marked by a plaque plunked in the corner.
Or so it claims. No one is sure if the exact location
is on the east or the west side. As populations grow,
cemeteries become valuable real estate, are relocated
to the other side of town, the land converted
into suburbs. Sometimes they move the headstones
but not the bodies. In cities, homeless are stacked
in a potter's field when they die. The ground unmarked.
It's easy for us to ignore what's buried underneath,
until we hear footsteps pacing locked rooms upstairs
and find chairs stacked neatly on the kitchen table.

David Mondedeu, *Sonnets of 40 Winter and 40 Springs*, photogravure

Ars Poetica for the Devil

For a night
he tapped
like the Devil

at my window,

as though
he wanted back

something I'd stolen.

Or maybe
he was only
a tree, lurching

in a windstorm —

This poem
was a tree

or the Devil,

tapping, and
in his hands
were choughs

dropping

gravel they took
for pecans.

I counted

the lightning's
distance,
turning, in

my open hand,

picked pecans, and
with the other

sketching the barehanded

Devil, alone now
the thunder'd driven
away his birds —

This was when

the poem was
his sweetest:

the Devil

standing in
his field,
as though

he wanted back

his birds,
suddenly

without

anything else
to do.
I drew

a salt circle

around my bed
and slept,

finally.

What else could
I have done?
This poem

was a tree,

a chough
in the hand,

or

he was
a bare hand —
and

what else is

a bare hand
but the Devil's,

tapping?

What else is
a poem
to him

as he goes

but
the thunder

of his leaving

and the thunder
that drove
away

those stupid birds

he once
loved?

Parable

A certain sycamore overlooks
a canal and a field of brittle corn
where against the cropland backdrop

a house far-off grays yearly, smoke
from bonfires of trimmings and rot often

blackening any vantage of the white-crowned
Dolomites. On this day,
no bonfires. A local boy stripped

and lowered himself
to swim in the canal and was sunk.

Ask him, and he'll say he remembers
only the now old sycamore, its split roots
tapping, standing there, grown

still against the Dolomites' stillness,

and his hands' nailbeds then
naked and blushing,

his father dressing him with kisses
and praying under the blue, bent
light of Bartholomew, fixed in glass.

Ask him: his own ceremonies
have since seemed less — cotton-ball handfuls
soaked with witch hazel

he holds to what of himself he can see
with a small mirror.
As if by a tightening of thread, he closes himself

to purify, after men are rough,
what he has been given.

As when Samuel poured a vial of oil
over the head of aimless Saul

and kissed him,

and this opened the eyes of God to Saul,
and God bent in from the gray morning sky
to watch.

Even the sycamore's heard the story:
Saul was given
a drove of donkeys,

the oak of Tabor, the goatherd
driving his tribe across
the terebinth woodland of Judea,

the gracious stranger who offered Saul
the bread he carried in his arms.

Ask the sycamore how the parable
moves, and he'll tell you: imprinted,

reprinted in small, determined
histories — the boy in the canal scanning
the water's undersurface,

the long, untraceable refraction
glittering with fistfuls of erupted light,

and sycamore seedlings,
helicoptering down, out of the visible air.

Mutius in the Garden of Rejection

There are five biblical gardens of significance, but more than twenty-five
gardens of significance in Rome

buried under other gardens of significance in Rome.

The biblical gardens of significance have not been buried, but God has
closed some of them.

There are no lyrebirds in Rome, but if there were, they would roost mostly
in the Vatican's English Garden and mimic the Fountain of the
Eagle's fixed hiss.

Lyrebirds are doltish songsters who, closed in a fox's mouth, go limp even
before the scrap is done.

Here are the major facts: lyrebirds must roost in low branches, unable as
they are, like chickens, to fly for very long,

and Mutius is given twenty-five words before his father casually kills him
with a sword.

Meanwhile, the Cantonese slang "25 boy" means "traitor." A small
coincidence.

Another: in my country, 2.5 is the percent of killings that are filicides.

Three of Mutius's last twenty-five words are the word "help," as are two of
his last three.

The five significant gardens of the Bible are the Garden of Rebellion, the
Garden of Rejection, the Garden of Redemption, the Garden of
Reception, and the Garden of Rejoicing. So many "Re-"s. As
though the Bible keeps trying to get gardens right.

Twenty-five, in biblical terms, signifies grace multiplied by grace—"Grace
upon grace"—which to some Christians means God calls back his
children by killing 100 percent of them.

Beside the temple in the Villa Borghese gardens, I bend down to dig.
     The uncovered soil smells like burnt olives, and I wield a toy
     spade

with the other tourists, revealing a fake archeological site:

buried gardens of the real Lucius Licinius Lucullus, who has, we're
     told, been memorialized by a strain of Swiss chard—a mild and
     sweet strain, one which holds well after cutting.

In my edition of *Titus Andronicus*, the stage direction is "Stabbing
     MUTIUS," but my edition of *Titus Andronicus* does not specify
     the number of times Mutius is stabbed.

My father knows why five is the biblical number for grace, and he
     knows how to multiply grace by grace, but I do not.

I dig in the foreign garden, where I want a lyrebird to be,

and a fox—a fox who knows the lyrebird can fly, but not for long, and
     that it can live for twenty-five years, but rarely does.

Whale Sounds

I knew not to tell you that Dad's jaw clicking means he's thinking, not angry, which is when his lips shrink into one thin line below his mustache, which is now because he's watching the road, clicking and shrinking, and the Starburst wrappers are crinkling too loudly so I open them slower. Starbursts because you reported a breakthrough, which means I dug my thumbnail deep enough into the spine to make actual tears when I told you something I knew you'd think was sad, so Dad buys Starbursts because he told us to be honest and a break-through means crying, which is honest, but I knew he didn't mean it. So I told you about Allison with cardboard boxes under her bed overflowing Butterfinger wrappers dripping blood when Mom told me to get her for our family movie Friday. We were at the part where the Emperor gets turned into a llama, so I pretended to be a llama because your eyes were bigger than most grownups', and your shoulder-length white hair was not Air Force, so either you're especially good at making me tell things I don't want to tell or you're an idiot, and I wanted to keep my groove. Allison's the reason Dad's clicking, because he wants her happy but doesn't know how much it costs; shrinking because he thinks it's the last week he'll see us. I want to tell him everything I didn't tell you, but all five pink Starbursts are clogging up my throat and, besides, the Air Force doesn't require him to ask the questions he isn't so set on getting answers to. My tummy makes whale sounds and my mouth begins to water; Dad's passing everyone on the highway and it feels like you're a car behind trying to hit us with a secret. You said This stays between us, but so did my friend Maureen when I told her about the rape and she said she wouldn't tell. But she did tell, because Vice Principal Skintags asked me why I said that I would cut her throat and I said I never told her I would slit her throat. He said cut, she said slit, I said slit; I said Fine: because it was a secret nobody was supposed to share but I had to tell someone. Nobody's falling for the We Keep Secrets game, Dr. Ivers. Mama told me what and what not to talk about, told me off for telling Maureen. We're driving to move Allison from the hospital to inpatient in Boise. Dad asked How did therapy go. I said Good, then fell asleep. We had this conversation for eight years until I went to college. You don't know that because we left Idaho together, as a family. I'm not sure what you wanted, but I know we didn't give it to you.

Planets to Go to with PTSD

When you were small
you were obsessed with blowfish.
You touched them gently with your fingers
and watched them puff up. Blowfish can't
hide anything. They use their own fear
to scare off things that hurt them.

Think about inhaling, and every trigger
in your body runs back to the gun
it came from. Guns melting
into black pools you can float in.
Imagine jumping off a cliff
and your hands still reaching for something
as you're falling.

The time you knocked your front
tooth out on a metal pole. You swore
nothing would ever hurt as much
as that did, and so you screamed
through blood.

You broke your foot when you were eleven.
You walked around with it for three days,
swelled up like a red flag, before someone
took you to the doctor. When you tell this story
you say this happened when you were twelve.
This seems like an appropriate age
to learn that pain is the one thing no one
can ever take away from you.

Think about forests as a place for
fire to come home to. Foxes and deer
scurrying through the trees/mice diving
into holes/owls trying to see through
smoke. Move like a beam of light in
order to survive.

Figure out how to fit the sun
into an accordion and play the
weight of a planet in your arms.

Think about little moons
gravitating their cold bodies
into view, silent and alive.

Ashley Inguanta, photograph

Hands Holding the Void (Invisible Object)

Each morning, after hot tea and a grapefruit half, my sister cloisters herself within her museum of youth—one wall of all Christmas cards received this decade, her vanity cluttered with every small toy sent by a father known only through an upside-down stamp, smudged thumbprint. For hours, she lies on the floor. On her stomach, she makes lists of fifty (colors, girls' names, cities), then folds each into a crane, before lighting their small heads afire to time the burn. On her back, she contemplates her bedside wall, covered in pictures of each cat lost (they run away after a year or two): Honey, Jasmine, Kassandra, before turning to the ceiling. Their leashes dangle from bellcollars, each stapled to the ceiling: a rainbow of ropes, each ending in a handnoose. *What medicine can stop these dreams?* By dusk, she stands at her window, watching shadows ripple across grass like the weight she never had. Her hands move over her hips, over concave space between each other: a bird circles the yew where her nest once was. *Nothing is*, she whispers, her eyes sheeted mirrors, gray an interminable blue.

Following I-64 West

Before leaving his old bedroom, he drops his grandfather's cross into his pocket.

His grandmother shouts from her lawn chair, *Don't forget to call. Tell me when you've crossed the time zone.*

After he leaves, his sister takes off her shoes, throws leftover corncobs into the field for deer, and sits on the back porch in his worn-out 4-H t-shirt to finish the jug of bourbon slush.

The radio offers only permutations of country: classic, contemporary, folk, rockabilly, bluegrass, Appalachian, religious, and a capella, all eventually fading, around Bluefield, into static.

Leaving West Virginia, it begins to rain. Hail like marbles, the tiger's eye lost on his last day of public school.

Late sunset, and he cannot distinguish mountains from thunderclouds.

He remembers conversations spurred toward the electric fence of God, everyone's hands in the air when his uncle stood and sang *Amazing Grace.*

After dinner, his grandmother and sister kept bringing out plates of dessert—cakes, pies, cookies, tarts—until the rented tables were filled, faces hopeful each time as if to say, *See, you cannot go and leave us with all this food.*

In Kentucky, the road cuts through hills, rock bluffs red and brown like carved meat.

He opens his suitcase beside the Ohio River and finds half his shirts missing to make room for his sister's cookies, watermarks on the notes inside each plastic bag telling him *strawberry, poppyseed, cinnamon.*

Crossing into Illinois, he writes to his sister, *You can feel the thunder here—it rolls for so long. I seem to always be saying I miss you.* Two days later, at the apartment, he gets a card from her, *In the hospital again. Wish you were here.*

On the first day of work, a bird flies into his office window. How quickly scarlet fades to copper.

Home sounds like the first day of hunting season. The edge of a crucifix pulled along skin. Bird eyes unbuttoning blood in the soft pop of cartilage, glass, and breeze.

Ashley Inguanta, photograph

Directing A Dream *and Unable to Speak*

After that rehearsal I was a hollow in the heart of a tree,
a blue sheet waved by two girls in lycra we called *ocean*
since our fool (sweet boy, baked cookies for Sunday practice,
and he made my name tremble like the echo in a seashell —

once he dropped to his stomach backstage, *Sit on my back,*
Feather, bet I could still do ten pushups, and the faeries gathered
as I rode, a hand on his shoulder and the other in the air,
eyes closed to savor, *house lights off, cue the prologue*), my villain,

late for his entrance, I found tangled with the Queen
and her Indian boy in the dressing room, heap of wings,
taffeta, silk. Already in mourning black, I did not turn

away as they jumped apart and dressed, did not take
the hands he held out to me, did not speak again that week
except to say, then, *Go on stage — time for your death scene.*

[list]

less the way i looked:
the way i made things
an alchemy a power
just behind the lips
how art can sweep
you up make you
riot the theater hurt
whoever's closest
that dissonance that
infection dug into
the lines you loved
you left me at the
subway i could see
it in small hungry
words before i
ever saw it at all

[measurements]

intervals in years, not decades or
more, missed, off—how could
you arrive so accurately and so
late? you said practice was the plan
but practice was the problem: you
led me like a horse by the mouth
you touched your ribs and felt mine
you bit your fingers and bit mine
there is a place behind the ear a
movement of the tendons in your
forearm there is a certain
number of bones in each spine
a certain magnitude of yes

For You Shall Be Called to Account

The ancestors of everyone I've let into my body
are gathered in a small room with one window,
no lights. Yes, the room is crowded. Yes, there
are no chairs. Yes, they are talking—why are we
here, says the Nazi resister. Where are the chairs,
says the Viking (no horns). Where is the light, say
the people with their new French name hung
around their necks heavy like a long black cross.
Here, says the grand wizard, and a long white
light descends in a point from the ceiling.

The people of the oldest empire are here, too,
they have brought their own fire (hidden), they
can speak French, they know in an instant not
to trust that light. They are opening a window.
How do we get away from these people, they
murmur. True Aryans! say the Nazis with their
new French name. No one is speaking
to the Catholics. There is a knock on the door—

there is a door. More Nazis. How did this happen?
Outside the open window there is a small huddle
of shawls and feet and candlesticks, a suitcase
and a cane. Someone has forgotten their things,
says the Nazi resister. The candlesticks turn into
my great-grandmother, their tarnish to coal smudges,
the cane grows tall into my great-zayde, the shawl
his mother, suitcase an uncle with an aunt inside.
The feet are just empty shoes—my cousins have
already died. The small huddle of my family outside
the open window begins to sink to a great distance,
first one storey, then a long drop. Someone spits
through the open window. My great-zayde
shields his face. Great-grandmother looks up.
What are those people, she says, doing
in that room?

For Every Animal of the Forest Is Mine

Later, when you said you were going to become a pastor, a forest
sprang up around us, thick and blue-dark; the ceiling of the hostel
gave way to branches, the legs of the bedframe split down into roots.
You said you were really into being good to women, and my namesake

cousin with her lantern took a small step out of the trees. I moaned
and you thought I loved it, the forest of ruinous Europe invisible
to you, my cousin not yet damp with tuberculosis, how wonderful
this vision of my still-living name among instant old Romania,

this village apparition, but her light did not touch the pool of our
blankets, and I did not see her mouth moving through the shreds
of my clothes that had caught in the forest canopy like birds
during the ascent of the trees. You are safe, you are cared for,

you said when I was on top of you and couldn't see the crows
shake their soft black heads. All of the other good women had
left already, this wasn't fair to you either, but day turned
into night and it was too late for me to leave the forest

and you had all the good women and God in a cart
waiting for you on the road. And my future self could see
this from a glass city, not yet soaked with pneumonia,
and along with the ghost of my namesake cousin

we had just reached through and pulled me out of those woods
but when I told you, I said the unspeakable thing and you balked,
I can't save you, you said, and there I was again on a blanket
in the forest and you were leaving, everyone was leaving,

you felt unsuccessful, you can't save a people who think
they are chosen, you left, our eyes wild, our yellow teeth, all
of us gleaming at you from the dark like animals, the forest I pulled
around me though neither the forest nor the road were safe for women
like me, the women you left, you reverend, some day.

Ginny Calabrese

Ginny, you'd never believe it.

It's 3 a.m. in the little downtown section of Woodside, Queens. Roosevelt Avenue, with the elevated #7 train galumphing overhead. Across from the 61st Street station, which makes this a major thoroughfare, or as major as a minor stretch of street in western Queens can be deep at night in the middle of the week, because at this station the two great arms of the MTA meet. Long Island Rail Road and New York City Transit, and if you look at it from just the right angle the Woodside station is a shoulder of sorts, a brawny beefy bulked-up weight-bearing crossbar of a hulk atop trapezial escalators and stairs that spew passengers onto the street at regular intervals, even now, this late, so it's generally a lively little scene.

Into which walk — Ginny, this is the part you'd never believe — two young fellows holding hands. By young I mean, oh who knows, 18? 19? By fellows I mean, that's right, Ginny, men. A couple of nellys is what you would have said. We don't call them that anymore. Sweet-looking youngsters. Why sweet? It's just that they don't have that he-man go-to-the-gym look, all pumped and glistening. They look, well, rather ordinary. Why wouldn't they, you might say, but no, you wouldn't, you'd know what I mean, how extraordinary their ordinariness seems to me. Just a couple of guys, college students probably, heading who knows where but that's not the point. This is: two boys holding hands. Walking down a late-night Queens street. Did I mention the area's chock-a-block with pubs? Filled to spilling with what look to be construction workers, recent arrivals from Ireland mostly, rough types with two-day stubbles constantly engaged in loud squabbles over soccer scores, politics, old family grudges. Or that — oh Ginny, I wonder what you'd make of this — it's illegal to smoke inside any public place nowadays, so there's always a solid line outside leaning up against the wall puffing cigarettes. So make that two boys holding hands walking past smoking drinkers outside bar after bar, toward the train station as waves of people tumble down the stairs and hurry along the street.

Ginny, nobody cares.

No one gives them a second glance. No one calls them a nasty name. Or touches them, or feints a fake jab to scare.

The wild part is that these two beautiful boys walking down the street with clasped hands apparently expect nothing else. They don't seem scared or nervous in the least. This all comes naturally to them, or that's how it looks to me.

I'm the old insomniac senior citizen dyke sitting in the Stop Inn Diner sipping tea. My usual booth at the window. Watching everything, as I do most nights. I've seen a lot, Ginny. Certainly my share of boys with boys and girls with girls. That's been my family. Starting with you and me. Yet this is one sight I've never before seen. I'm talking about the ease of it, the unremarkability. In the middle of the night. In Queens.

I'm not saying everything's perfect for our kind. The fact I'm surprised here means this same-sex PDA is still not the norm, at least not outside some few streets in the Village, Chelsea, Park Slope, or, I don't know, I've heard certain suburbs like Montclair or Nyack. But it is a new world in many ways, Ginny. As I sit here and watch the cute young couple blithely walk hand in hand to the Woodside train station, I feel an irresistible urge, one I've felt must be a million times over all these years. An urge to turn to you, to say lookee there, ask you what you think.

You might not be surprised to hear how I've missed you. But Ginny, you'd never believe it: so long afterward, I still can't get used to the world without you.

✿   ✿   ✿

Do you remember our first time? We were aquanauts, swimming deep in unexplored seas. Crazy. Wow. That was some hot sticky heat. We did this scissory thing—remember, G?—with our legs on top of and also underneath. I mean, we didn't know, we were making it up, mashed up against each other so that our wet sponges, our sweet girly pretties could meet, and they did, that's how open we were to each other, how, I don't know, brave is what I think, no guides, the uncharted deeps, our red pink raw slithery selves slurping singing speaking in tongues down there in the unplumbed briny oceanic depth, I mean god, Ginny, it was sweet, two suction cups clamped onto each other sucking sliding kissing between our scissored legs. Meanwhile our mouths exploring everywhere else. I remember your tongue tasted of banana, that was the bubblegum you'd just spit out. Your brown nipples where I laid my lips faintly fruity, ever so slightly like strawberry wine, that cheap wine we used to sneak sips of behind the John Jay High School bleachers on Saturday nights. My lips loving your nipples so much they wouldn't leave, they wanted to stay there for all eternity: oh Ginny, oh my sweet lost lovely, what they did to you, what they've done, god, G my wonder girl forever first love.

Ginny, can you see it still like I do? How we kissed, down deep and up above, how we scissored and swam, and rode, until you reared up, threw your head back, your fine small head pretty pinched face sharp nose dark darting eyes and I threw my torso forward clasped my hands behind your neck our chests smacked sweaty breasts the scissoring the sponges absorbing each other colliding colluding joined. We were swimming. Seesawing. We bit each other's lips so we wouldn't scream. Remember how we came shooting to the surface, G, divers aquanauts explorers exploding up from the unknown deeps? Think about it, what nerve we had, what faith, what hope. We were 16, Ginny. You and me.

❈ ❈ ❈

Next week I'll be 79. Fifty years you're gone. I think about you always. And I'll always remember that scissory deep dive we did there in your bedroom in November 1951 in Park Slope, Brooklyn. Not just the way everyone recalls their first time. And not because no one else has ever again suctioned me so powerfully, vacuumed me so absolutely clean, drawn so much feeling from the depths of me, scooped me, rawed me. What stays with me is your face as you reared up and drew back. It's the face I force myself to see when some TV story about you assaults me or I open the newspaper and discover another 10 years have passed and there's a front-page feature on the anniversary. I grab the remote and click off the TV; fold the paper, tear it in strips and dump it into the re-cycling bin. Squeeze my eyes shut and refuse to see the you made famous by pain, by horror, the contorted features screaming mouth gushing blood I've pictured how many nights in the futile struggle to forget, to sleep. Ginny the victim, Ginny the symbol, Ginny the martyr of Kew Gardens, Queens. Ginny Calabrese, whose name means what the hell is wrong with people, poor girl, though what was she doing out so late at night alone? No. I close my eyes and see instead the true you, dashing undersea explorer, legs scissored with mine, reared up, leaning your head back, cradled by my hands. Gasping for breath. Fresh fine 16-year-old Ginny, hippest smartest sassiest of the Calabrese clan, crazy grin spreading crookedly across your face as you stare at me and I stare back until I can't stand the wait and I tighten my grasp and pull you in toward me and just before our breasts crash you lift your hands and cradle my face and soundlessly mouth my name in all its varieties—Lillian Lily Lil—and I'm thrilled again I'm back.

Not this haggard old wilt but fresh young yours. I'm me again with you. With my eyes closed, at least. When I block out the world and what it did. When I see the you I knew.

I'm yours, G, that night in Brooklyn with your life in front of you. I'm yours tonight, long after the end. Gee, I want to hear you say my name again.

Forget the other. I won't let it define you. First love. Best friend. This is who you were and will always be. This is the true Ginny Calabrese.

※　※　※

And yet. Who do I think I'm kidding? They took the true you long ago. I'd have to be a wizard, waving a wand over a magic cabinet with a fake back panel the size of the world, to make Ginny Calabrese the myth disappear.

The frozen moment. The cautionary tale. Lesson: Ladies, watch yourselves. Pivot point of the '60s. A turn.

March 1964. One assassination down, many more to come— depends how you count, Dr. King of course, and RFK, but Medgar Evers too, Malcolm X, Che, Fred Hampton, oh Ginny, so much happened, and it moved me. I changed. I think you would have too. I, and yes I see the irony, got involved. I had to. It was partly for you. I'm not saying the name Ginny Calabrese ranks up there with these terrible events, epoch-changing tragedies, but it has its place in the sweep of that decade. My private memories can't compete with what the world has made of you. Your last hour does define you. Perhaps it defines all of us, ever since. That's some legacy, G. But you were a tough cookie. Strong back, lugging those crates of beer up from the bar's cellar every night.

So which story is it? The one about the 38 windows? The courtyard as amphitheater, the rapt spectators? For 50 years

I've tried to understand them. See them as human, at least, for surely the turning away can't be equated with the deed itself. They weren't the monsters. They didn't do it. Something there is in people that stops their hands, snatches them back when they instinctively reach out. Something that says I don't want to get involved. Known since that night as the Ginny Calabrese Syndrome. Yet I still so want to believe that the first impulse is to help. That the turning away isn't innate, and can be untrained.

The screams. The answering silence. The scar on the Kew Gardens name. The shame. The blot. The what on earth were they thinking. The 38 windows.

Try as I might to close my eyes, another part of me is driven to draw aside the curtains and peek. Who were they? Why didn't they act? For though the story is about a girl—a woman, thank you very much, but she didn't live long enough to become a feminist, which I've no doubt she would have—it is also, yes, I admit the world has it right, about the onlookers. About what it means that they let her die.

She fought. She did everything she could, oh god she wanted to live. She called out, her voice weakening as blood pumped onto the pavement.

Wait. It's too soon. The crimson too bright. I'm not ready. I want to think now not of her weakness, but her strength. Ginny the streetwise city gal, barkeep, she of the stunning slantways smile, Ginny zooming through the quiet Queens streets in her little red Fiat. An active participant in every living moment, not a symbol, and if the moments include her last she must still be the fulcrum around which the whole thing revolves. This much she is due. If not the hero, for there's no inherent heroism in being stabbed to death, the focus at least.

I wish I could rectify the freezing of Ginny the person into Ginny the concept. What they've made of her. Pick your academic discipline. Criminology: uninvolved onlookers, liability of. Journalism: hidden witnesses, unreliable memory, objectivity, impossibility of. Psychology: dissociation, groupthink. Sociology: urban crime, fear of the other. Literary analysis: subjectivity of language, screams as gender-encoded text. She'd have mocked it all, "Whatchu talkin about," she'd have drawled in her best exaggerated Brooklynese, toothpick cocked out of uplifted right corner of her lopsided smile. "Nobody here but us regular types." A person.

A woman, who laughed sang spit drank, gristly and tenderhearted, who would have, I think, become so much more if she'd had her full years. But who didn't.

❖ ❖ ❖

Things I've seen on the subway: a Wall Streeter put on deodorant, reaching under her blouse, giving a quick swish at each armpit, returning the stick to her briefcase; a man in pajamas and bunny slippers read the *Financial Times*; a woman, gray-haired and spindly as vermicelli, squat and defecate—well, this one was on the platform, not the actual train; a teenaged boy, some sort of human piano wire, stand on his hands, then his head, and then leap at a pole, grip it, and thrust his legs out until they stiffed perpendicular to the floor, and stay like that, hanging straight sideways like a flag frozen in sleet, for a good three minutes. I've many times seen rats rummage along the tracks. I've seen lovers hold hands and kiss and lonesome souls watch as something, it's seemed I could actually see it happening, gave way inside them, some internal avalanche as hope or at least the ledge where it might perch gave way and toppled toward oblivion.

But I had never seen, until one day a year ago this week, an act of human kindness so simple yet complete that it nearly dropped me to my knees. In gratitude, I mean. For I have found in these long decades since Ginny died that I need a good deal of help if I am not to dwell in a generalized state of rage and rancor, and also that the aid almost always arrives from an unexpected source. A stranger. Random individuals who do some kind deed, usually a slight thing that holds no import for anyone but me and may not even involve me in any way, because, and this is my saving grace, truthfully it doesn't take all that much to raise me back to some semblance of faith in humanity. Each person who has by word, action, or, let's be honest, gesture, expression, shampoo smell, in some unfathomable fashion restored me to my better self, each of them has my thanks but not only that. I recently read that your brain retains a permanent image of every face your eyes have ever seen, and that in the case of New Yorkers who ride the subway to and from work every day the number of these faces typically reaches millions. So there is not only in my mind a sense of having been rescued in so many ways day after post-Ginny day, of having been given hints, prompts, provisions that like clothes and food to refugees made it possible for me to proceed; there is also in my brain, bundled into the numberless folds, fired along the trillions of neuronal connections, the visage of every one of these my saviors.

It's a funny comfort to know that although, just one year later, I cannot clearly call up the details of their features, they are locked, everlasting albeit inaccessible, in a living piece of me. The woman who rolls through the cars of the #1 train asking for money. And the fellow who one day helped.

She is terribly disabled—it's hard to see exactly how because of the way she drapes her coat but most likely she has no legs—and very poor, obviously, for why else would she resort to this survival technique? And she is angry. Set upright atop a small wooden plank, a platform on wheels, holding two short lengths of PVC piping with which she pushes against the floor so that the wheels roll and propel her forward through the crowded train, her eyes about even with most people's knees. Unlike others who try to collect some dollars on the trains—homeless men with AIDS, runaway teens, former prisoners who make little speeches about how no one will hire them, undocumented immigrants singing sad songs of home and flashing photos of a child awaiting surgery— the rolling woman doesn't say anything. She just pushes the PVC pipes against the floor, rolls a foot or two, stops, picks up the coffee can set next to her on her platform, lifts it and shakes. If no one responds, and for some reason it does seem that she inspires a sort of dread in many people so that most make every effort to ignore her, then she lifts it higher, shakes it louder, and tilts her chin up so as to make eye contact with those in seats. She narrows her eyes, thrusts the coffee can, shakes, stares, and stays thus poised until someone coughs up. She doesn't let off the folks standing at the poles either. She rolls herself right at them, she actually nudges their ankles with the cart or their knees with her donation can. It takes a determined, in my view, a determinedly hard-hearted son of a banker—and I mean that literally, this is after all a train full of Stock Exchange folk and if most of them are, like I was till I recently retired, secretaries, messengers, low-level clerks and the like because, come on, the rich don't ride the subway, still there are always some suits among the mix—to withstand her tactics. Most dig into pocket or purse and drop something in. Eventually she moves along. When she exits a train car to roll along the platform to the next there is a nearly palpable drop in the tension level.

I'm no saint. I too feel relief when she leaves, if only because
her presence, the routine she's forced to carry through, feels to me
like such a rebuke of everything that is failed in our society. So
many well-dressed office workers. So many busy on their smart-
phones. Nearly everyone plugged in to a private music playlist. In
our midst someone too poor to own a wheelchair and what do most
of these iPeople wish? That she disappear.

But one day a year ago this week when the rolling woman
came through my car on the #1 train, someone sang a different
tune. And I have to confess that I am so easily swayed, I'm such
a creature of moods, always have been, as Ginny would no doubt
testify, yes I descend with such unwarranted ease into the thickest
unlit fathoms but also am so susceptible to such swift feathery as-
cension, that this someone's single small act affected me powerfully.
In fact, in the days and weeks that followed it drove me deep into
contemplation, giving me the kick in the teeth I needed to finally
get off my butt and retire (onto my butt is I suppose more apt)
and, after that, the wherewithal to think harder about Ginny than
I've ever allowed myself. I've never stopped thinking of her, yes it's
true, but now I found myself ready to really see. Face the finish, I
mean. Not flinch. Not shrink. And consider whether there might
be an after, after all, for me.

Because it doesn't matter how many years Ginny's gone, it
all happens again every day. I love her we're wild we break we're
tight she dies I live I love others we break I love again but tight?
Tightly tied, body and mind? No, never another. What does it
mean, what does it say about me that I could only have one best
friend in my life and that after 50 years without her she's still it?
What went wrong with me, and if I blame it on what happened to
Ginny then how do I go on, or, really the question is, have I? Ever
lived again? If everything always comes back to her, can I call all
these days of mine a life? Or has it been one long stall, and can the
stall halt at this late date? Is there still a way to recommence?

I know that (duh, as the kids say) when I talk about Ginny
I'm talking about me. But I'm also talking about the world—to the
world, and it's a plea as much as anything else.

Please, fellow Earthlings. I probably have no right to ask but
I'm asking. Do not turn away from a person in need. I can't prove
it—I'm no scientist—but I think that when you do some part of
your brain stops firing. You know how there's less than one-half of

one percent of our genome that makes humans a different species from chimpanzees? Well, I think that's the part that's compromised when compassion shrivels and dies. I'm not saying chimps aren't compassionate, elephants, some other beasts. But I'm talking about the animals that walk upright and tie their shoes with opposable thumbs and talk in a thousand tongues and understand quantum theory and are so primitive, so undeveloped backward unevolved that they can hear a girl cry out as she's stabbed chased beaten raped for an hour or more, they can listen and do nothing. This is the quandary I finally have to face. And all it took, a year ago on the IRT, was a young dreadlocked man to remove his earbuds, stand, bend to the disabled woman on the cart, ask her could he give her a hand, pick up her coffee can and walk the train car from end to end murmuring a quiet appeal, come on, folks, hey, be nice, come on, let's help a sister out, then return the can to her filled to the brim. When she tried to thank him he ducked his head and said "no big thing" and when the train entered the next station she rolled herself out, her face a map of stupefaction.

I too was flabbergasted. A sad statement because, really, he was right, it was no big thing. Took him all of two minutes, cost him nothing, time, energy, money—and yet I'd never seen the likes of it and fear I never will again. It made me think. About Ginny, and me, and those I-don't-know-what-to-call-thems who lived in the Millbridge Arms on Austin Street in Kew Gardens, Queens. About her killer, who lives on, imprisoned. Which in a way is how I've thought of myself, a prisoner of loss, a sort of amputee, the pith of me cut out by her death, which means he half-killed me too. Only I didn't die.

❖ ❖ ❖

Retreat to a safer place. Back to the bedroom. No sex. We're innocents yet: 1950. The two of us best pals, Ginny and Lil, at 15.

Light streams in the window. Greenish rays, a slight viridescence as if dispatched from Prospect Park several blocks to the east. Refracted sunshine, then, bends through a grassy prism decidedly exotic in our paved, populous Brooklyn. Or so it looks in memory. Perhaps I'm imparting a retroactive verdant glow where none shone. Confusing the ordinary sunshine that lit her room to Ginny's own radiance. Which I also, perhaps, exaggerate.

Though I don't think so. Ask anyone who knew her. Anyone. Our teachers at John Jay, well, I suppose they're most all dead by now as, Jesus, most everyone she ever knew may be, 50 years on. Is this what compels me now? A panic that soon she'll breathe in no one's living memory? I can't leave her to textbooks, senior thesis fodder. Ginny supine, splayed, carved, cracked, the concrete surrounds sprayed with her blood, this the only image of my dearest girl ever unto eternity. No. Surely someone survives. Some nonagenarian who had her in English or History, long since retired but sharp still if wobbly. Someone to testify to the pyrotechnic luminescence that was Ginny Calabrese.

Wisecracking. Gum-smacking. Crackerjack with a sharp comeback. No cheerleader, no apple-for-the-teacher kiss-up, rarely the first hand raised except to ask for a hall pass. Ginny in the bathroom sneaking a smoke, Ginny in detention for smoking in the bathroom. Ginny the shocker with painted red toenails plucked arched eyebrows short cropped hair. Bermuda shorts in her locker; she'd change the instant the last bell rang at the first hint of warm weather. Unbutton the bottom of her sleeveless shirt and tie it at her navel so she could bounce homeward unfettered by fabric. Toss her little curls to catch a breeze. No, our girl was not the honor roll type. Yet I challenge you to find a teacher still alive who will not positively glow speaking of Ginny Calabrese. Found themselves giving her B's and afterward wondering why when her work didn't merit it. Chiding themselves for losing objectivity.

She got under a person's skin.

So there we are, two skinny teens, lying on her bed in bra and underpants because fashion designers had not yet invented bikinis, slathered with baby oil, her mother's most raggedy old towels under us to sop up the grease, positioned precisely under the sun's rays on a warm May Saturday. Tanning, side by side. Her forearms' bristly brown hairs wisping against my skin. I remember the tickle, and shivering, and wondering why in that heat, and how the first inchoate glimmerings of a guess at what was going on tingled my spine, and how I stiffened then. I remember inching away, shifting ever so slightly beyond her arm whiskers' reach. Dread of the precipice, unarticulated in my 15-year-old head, which is how I want it to stay. Everything as it was. Ginny and me reclined on her bed, warm Saturday in May. She'd stacked a pile of 45s onto the little portable record player atop her dresser. So there we are, sunbathing teens, snapping our fingers, waggling our feet, singing along to single after single through the long lazy afternoon. Frankie Laine. Patti Page. The Ames Brothers.

There's a move from the '90s called *Afterlife*. Japanese. The crux: everyone, when they die, goes initially to a sort of cosmic stage set where they are asked to name the one perfectly happy time of their life. More precisely, they're asked to pick a moment or scene, an hour, a day, a lived experience from their now unalterably finite life, that so embodied joy or contentment, excitement or passion, whatever the feeling they would want once more to feel, that, given this one final opportunity they would choose to inhabit it again, fully, finally and for all time. Many opt for childhood: a day at Disneyland, a birthday party, riding a bike. Some reach even further back and sink against mother's breast, suckling, sighing, unaware of any sensation but bliss. For others, it's romance: a hand held, a first kiss. Whatever it is, the crew reproduces the scene. It's surprisingly crude. A cheap facsimile, cobbled together with whatever ridiculous props are at hand. There's a pilot who wishes to be aloft again amid the billowy white clouds, and they provide the fakest-looking wooden contraption into which he climbs and the cheesiest possible cotton-balls-glued-together agglomeration, a kindergartener's approximation of clouds, which they bounce in the air around his "cockpit" by means of an electric fan. Somehow, the fact that the whole re-enactment is manifestly fake matters not a whit. Each of the recently deceased is swept up utterly. At the climax, as the feeling hits its fullest pitch, they disappear. They are swallowed into infinity, existence terminated permanently, at the precise instant that they relive their most cherished sensation. Just before they fade the camera pans in on each face. We see a sweep of emotion that every time I watch, and I've seen this movie let's just say more than once, convulses me in weeping. I think of that May Saturday on Ginny's bed in our underwear by the window sunning and singing along as the 45s played. That's where I'd dwell, if the universe gave me such an opportunity, in my last instants as a conscious entity.

※ ※ ※

I'm circling. For fifty years this has been my M.O.: a quick, darting approach then backpedal to somewhere else. It's not denial.

Her exit was blood-soaked, I know. Of course I know. But, Ginny, can you blame me if I'd rather remember around it? Perhaps it's my own private variation on Ginny Calabrese Syndrome. I'd have helped if I could—I'd have gotten involved—but what can I do now, at this remove?

You'd be impatient, wouldn't you, G? Get to the heart of things, you'd tell me. My point exactly, dearie. You're the heart. The living Ginny. Not the shell enshrined in history. The girl I was gay with. Who taught me to be me.

I wonder sometimes how accurate my memory of that and other such sunny Saturday afternoons can possibly be. You shared a room with your sister, Patty. Three years younger. In and out all the time, bugging us, her own friends trailing after her, skittery prattling 12-year-olds bouncing on her bed, weaving cat's-cradle strings, or outside jumping rope on the little square of paved patio beneath the bedroom window. How she and her preadolescent crew tried our patience. Your brothers Anthony and Tru left us alone. Anthony, soon to turn 18, was headed for the army after graduation day. Tru was the baby, just finishing kindergarten. An accident, you liked to crack. Reprehensibly—Christ when I think of how clueless we used to be it staggers me, sometimes I think a need to atone for your baby brother's name is what to this day motivates me to attend the annual candlelight vigil outside the UN on Hiroshima Day—your folks named their youngest for the greater glory of President Harry S. Truman in honor of his atomic atrocity against the people of Japan.

The last time I saw the Calabreses was in the courtroom. September 1964. Anthony sat immobile, erect. Wedged against the wall in the front row of immediate family. Tru was on the aisle. The two stared straight ahead, jaws set, bookending their weepy parents and fidgety Patty. I didn't want to look at them. I couldn't stop looking at them. Searching for bits of Ginny in their faces. As I've searched for her, everywhere, ever since.

See how this keeps unraveling? I start in a long-before better place—the apartment, her room, happy day, cheery May—and before I know it I've traveled, vroom, warp speed, to the crime scene, and after. Toting up the damage. The decades.

I can circle all I want. Drive the express loop in hopes of avoiding the stench, the mess, the jammed-up hub—but inevitably I'm drawn to the center. The core's centripetal force drawing me in, down, till I smell her fear, hear her screams. So I detour. Back to the bedroom. This is how I've lived for 50 years. There's me, young, with Ginny, stripped to our undies on her bed, broiling in a thin slip of sun. And here's me. Old. Solitary. Here now and there then, never, if I can help it, in between. Sipping tea deep at night in a Queens diner, listening to Frankie Laine on a bright Brooklyn afternoon. My mind ever whirling, roaring a circuitous route, raising the volume on those twirling 45s sounding their tinny refrains to drown out her impossible-to-bear last sounds.

❊ ❊ ❊

Tonight, though, the whirring slows. Something about these handsome hand-holding boys I've spotted walking to the #7 train in late-night Queens. The grin I see them share as they pass the diner's window. Their fearless saunter. It stirs me. The old impulse hits, I want to turn, say, look, Ginny, do you see? Only this time, instead of my usual crash to pain at the thought of your name, my usual descent to that night, then the pulling away, around, circling back to the perfect day of ancient memory, I sit with the thought of you as you might be now. Here, sipping tea at the Stop Inn Diner in Woodside, Queens. An old ruin like me. If you'd been luckier, you'd be.

We'd watch the young couple pass and wonder together at the change the years have wrought. We might wax a bit smug at our own small roles, brag how we'd marched, who we'd fought, what we'd won.

I'm not smug but in truth I did all that. Without you. With others. Marched, fought, lost, won. The living went on although throughout I thought it did not. These boys prove it. It's not that everything's done. It's that the world—that even I, gap in my gut—carried on.

I want to tell the guys their grins remind me of you. I want to tell you look what we did. Look at them. They're you. They're me. After all this time, Ginny, you'd never believe it: look at us, we're alive, we're young.

ficus

From a list compiled by Wikipedia *of terms for gay in different languages, "ficus" is the literal meaning of the Swedish term "fikus," and is derogatory.*

You are as you are with a bonsai.
Persistent, you bring back life.
Its brown edges waning, you point to green,
blow kisses in its direction. You're as proud
as if it came from your contractions.
You pulled us over to the side of the road,
from a typical night in Vegas, you came back
to the car with two mini-trees, and waved
goodbye to the desert-burnt arborist.
Determined not to lose this one, you gave
healthy soil, adjusted the water and your
attachments—you balanced the light.

Five Sapphics for Three Young Men

getting into a big car. Two back, one front.
Bodies fluid on a hinge like a screen door.
Bodies in the summer breeze, errant, sexy,
Hawaiian, one seems.

I've been walking, heavy with an old desire.
I'm old enough, I carry love and doses.
Take me with you, today is sunny, fervent,
I could ride shotgun.

It looks like lunch brought you out, I see the bags,
sodas in hand, where to go from here? This is Friday,
maybe we could drive beyond the day, skip work,
shed our clothes beachside.

But you're gone now; the street yawns under the sun.
Bodies have a law their own. I turn, walk on.
Maybe it was chemical, the way I gazed,
wanted you, transfixed.

I slog uphill, homeward bound, the fog far out
begins to reach the spindly signal tower
above Twin Peaks. I always prefer the dream.
My cat waits, sleeping.

Bitter Melon Soup

My Chinese mother-in-law
beckons us to suburbia
where we journey to receive

this thin yellowish brew
that's steeped for days.
Good for cancer, she tells me,

and then in Cantonese
to Jason, begins
to explain the process

of how to boil bones
and slice with precision
the oblong, warty melons,

to create the mix and
allow the proper time
for the blend to become

what it must. Forever *gweilo,*
I don't know the words
of her plosive language,

only that she's called upon
old and trusted powers
of harmony, and healing,

that her sons smile at
her faith in rote rhythms,
when on holidays she bids us

to place oranges at family graves,
light incense, bow three times
as she whispers to the departed.

I remember her silence
when we stood alone
a few minutes together

outside Bank of America
the day her husband died.
I tried to say with my eyes,

I'm sorry,
and hoped they said as well,
He was a good man.

Now I raise the soup to my lips
as Jason's brother watches,
amused, cringing to see my first sip.

He's tasted it before, shuns it,
but says, *More power to you.*
Yes, it's bitter, but rich too

like a breeze over a cemetery slope
bearing traces of wavering smoke
that rises from offerings for the dead.

Epithalamium

We had a ritual. We met
across this meandering river in the open field
      feral with bindweed and Saint Augustine grass
and fucked in his van.

      Today, I am alone and wandering
this scrabbled creek. What used to be submerged —
      sand and crushed shells,
what counts for soil in Florida —
are the trails I walk on. Mosquitos drink
      what little oasis I am.

Birdcalls and the piercing screech
      of insects all around, like the moldering green

smell, yet I can still hear what I allowed him
to call me, remember how I rippled with pleasure
in his hands like algae on wavelets.

Before this river was redirected, it joined two others
      and flowed into the Gulf.

What we cannot change, we evade
      and call new. Call delay. I could
call the irrigation works at the headwater bog
         an aubade
      against flooding.

      Loneliness:
         What I could not change.
I didn't care not knowing his name.
      I called him Law. Law was a swarm of
      words my mouth wanted. *Clean. Discreet. No face*
no chat.

      I could say his chest was harbor.
I could say his touch was rebel

and renewed me. Love was never said
nor written down. I miss it
when my spirit blurs and I cannot see myself.

I failed to move the ritual.
Law said, *I feel free out here.*
Under him, I could sometimes forget a man
was lynched somewhere in this creek
at the beginning of the century
I was born in.

Lavender lavishes itself in humus.
Buzzards hover like villains in the rafters of an opera.
I confess this is not flesh anyone (myself included) has wanted.

Once when neither Law nor I could get off, I told a joke:
Why are all black people ontologists?
Because we have to keep proving we're human.
It didn't go over very well.

Moving off the trail, I wade into the river.
Time, like the sunset, feels suspended.
My bare feet
shuffle pebbles like some shore bird
grubbing about. An arrowhead clips my heel,
a little blood flowing
toward thickets of sweet bay and titi.

In some vista beyond my seeing, like the creek glazed by morning fog,
all this will be gone.
Gone the paths and signs, gone the milkweed, gone
the armadillos and the field,
gone the lynching tree when the river rejoins the others
and washes this away —
                              no, not gone
but come together, history, nature, love and loss
brought to proper scale in a glorious
algal bloom, a brightness of jade and amber,
all this water moving toward where it's always meant to,
where I cannot be, where I am.

At the Grave of Zora Neale Hurston

I kept my mad hound, Zora.
We wandered many miles,
pollen and dust staining us
the gold of ancient idols.

I got wet dog under my fingers.
He smells like me now, too,
you see he's carried roadkill
all the way here—raccoon,

then possum, hitched a fawn
five miles north, buried a fox
outside of town—it's in the blood
of his teeth. He found me, too,

by the roadside. Followed me
ever since. That first night,
I saw myself as that hound
licking my own face clean.

That morning, a distant cousin
gave me his gun, told me
to kill it. I couldn't shoot him.
Anything that loves you will

lay down for you or know enough
to fake it. I'm a coward in my life,
unlike my work. I don't know
which is worse. So many things

are conspiring to kill me, Zora.
Not only sickness and guns
but the tongues of those who
would sooner kiss me or call me

lover. Zora, it's not my dying day.

Lines We Draw

after Benjamin McVey and Ryan Walsh

The towers, he said, when he finally could image them, became the line
between, the negative made positive.

The river is bent by rocks, by gap, by breach, folded, messed with until
it doesn't even look like itself.

Could she, from between the towers of her life (is she allowed the
image of towers?) take something to pull her forward?

On the river bridge, people stop and watch the rush and spray.
She is on the other side, looking for the line after.

Is the water uneasy? After all, they took something as beautiful as
a cloud and made it mean warehouses of servers, made people look
down —

She would have liked to have shown a daughter how to tie a shoe, how
to print the alphabet.

After the towers fell, the sky filled with paper, drawers and drawers
and drawers, and drawers-worth of paper, tailless kites, whitecaps of a
troubled lake, white pendulums, wind-pushed empty swings.

After the bridge fell, the river resumed its line, untroubled, even
unchanged. How can that be?

She would have liked to have been drawn for. But it was right she had
no daughter.

On the riverbank, an oak table stands on fluted legs, chairless, opened
for its leaf.

Life Drawing, After Nightmare

just a dream,
    honey, just a
        dream. draw yourself
    through the room
of heartbeat. make
five minutes to
    hang on with
        the light scurry
        of the pencil
            the brush sound
                of the hand
                    adjusting like wind
                        to snow, sand
                            to ocean, as
                            the hand draws
                        the line across
                    and returns to
                show you where
            you are in
        relation to the
    others, the model
who breathes, the
paper, the line
you make of it.

The Thinnest String

Talk was small and laundry hung on string
          across the kitchen. Morning light, like woald,
dyed your hair and our walls with its rising.

You hummed threads of songs while ironing
          a shirt. Forgiveness had been thin, a camisole.
The back door was held open with string

so our orange cat could spend the morning
          on the stoop. I cracked four eggs on a bowl's
thin rim; the yolks intact, each rising
like a brass button in the glair.

                              Then you were mending
a tear in my jeans and one in the shoulder
of your favorite shirt.
                    Imagine heat as string:
with steam, you fixed my chiffon dress, threading
water through each wrinkle.
                              Like a thousand pressed stoles,
the sky was clean: new cloth, taut and rising.

Breakfast almost ready, the eggs sizzling
in the pan.
                    The sun was just a pinhole;
the wind, a needle closing up a seam. Clouds, rising
and so threadbare I could hear the snapping strings.

Life in Venice

Boys will not be boys for all the needlelace.
Blame the cheesecloth for calling the lambswool cashmere.
Whipcord wouldn't let the plowboy tow the line
into heaps of mist and updrafts of corn and hope.
It's easy to confuse Tussar silk with sendal.
In the gondola sunset envoys in paisley oppress
local wind-torn leggings in a rainbow of microfibers
so catching. You say enough gabardine trolls to last a lifetime
and they heard you. The bellboy in flannelette with airguard trim
and performative patches of herringbone and Grenfell cloth
breaks hearts. No one wants to talk about it how
cloying fools would glue in place the Point de Venise
full of a fleet of withdrawn offers meddled with
only in the imagination before the ripstop runners
suffuse the world in blackouts of yellow and red
and refunds hook them in enlightened spaces
coordinated checkers and medicinals ditch the forest
span the stunt to omit to optical clairvoyance
the blown pattern leaking secrets, returning as if home
summoned and studied, postponed ribbons and other irrational
mystics slide underneath, helpless to themselves and the memory of lawn
in general, the outlook continental. The boy encounters
the boy before the grammar, untidies and mucks without a blame
or blackmails around the festival. Verification proceeds.
Caffeine persists past the corduroy of bishops and wash of puzzles,
leagues of sailcloth and satin, embroidered names and numbers.

Pond Boys

A pinky promise in the dark
on an ugly blue and white couch
with our lips entangled and our feet,
and our hands gripping each other's hair
like reins, like the net to pull the fish in
from the pond by your uncle's house
with our shirts off and our jeans low
and our eyes crinkled in the sun,
and our cheeks red from each other.
With your tongue around my tongue and
my teeth, and a sting, and you bit me,
and my blood is swimming like the fish
in the net in your hands
on your body on the grass
with the dirt-spattered kneecaps
and the blood-ridden chest.
My blood can tell me how your mouth tastes,
but your taste is long gone, buried in a cigarette butt
at the bottom of the pond, in the hole in the dirt,
in your muddy, tangled hair and your eyes
and your lips and in your crooked teeth.

Love Story

Traditional love stories
have never been my style.
From princes and princesses,
to Romeo and Juliet.
I always preferred the plays with the cross-dressers,
and the fairy queen in love with a donkey.
Because at least they were different,
odd,
queer,
like me.

Misgendered

I see it
written in cursive
on a piece of cardboard
taped to my door.
I did the lettering myself,
but the curving font still cuts me.
I can feel it under my skin.
Behind my eyelids.
This is not my name.

dolores at midnight

kylie and i sail down the
slide on a blanket airplane
her man bearded and
whiskey-handed at the bottom

i think i'm
in love she says when
he walks away and i drink
to that

and i drink to the fact
that this slide is exactly as
narrow as my hips are wide
and i drink to our park
in the middle
of the night and the bruises
i know i'll wake up with

Ashley Inguanta, photograph

meat

this morning i drove
to greenbae to meet
the man who's going
to shape me.
❀❀

it's night and i've missed
the avocado, sliced
right into the meat
of my palm, drunk
on company wine.
//

he had said he's never had
an emergency; no transfusions.
❀❀

i am the smallest ball
on the white recliner,
cut hand cradled in the other.
try my best not to drip or
pass out while hannah
handles the kitchen
without letting me see
how much blood
there really is.
//

i asked him how he decides
where the nipples go and
he described a scene in which
my unconscious body is sat
up and the surgical team
measures me through
squinted eyes, like art hung
not quite straight—just a little
to the left, maybe up?

there it is.
and then here i am,
with this body
forever.
❀ ❀

i go to sleep with a pink
princess bandaid and the
intimate feeling that i have
insides, that there's
stuff beneath this skin and
that this stuff is
and is not
what makes me.
//

Sentence

Soon I will be a cliff face
of black type diving off into white
space — a full stop of my own
design — and I will wither
across the page into flesh
or laminated wood, or out
from monitor rays in photon
form, a post-mortem in flight
to be soaked in cloth or bone
or eye; I will be vibrations
and compression, a buzz
and a hum, a phonic familiar,
sonic ink — yet, to end, to be
that *will be*, is a terrifying
prospect, and I wonder
if I could have been music,
the long draw of the bow across
the strings, playful quavers
in the key of B♭, something flitting
and floating across the air,
perhaps a rondo over the
sand of the Sahara.

Composite Sketch

A pause. She takes my face in her hands, tells the officer his nose is thinner than mine, *He looks just like this one*, she says, *only healthier, normal, not so dark*. The man's hands tremble as she explains this. The page between us is gray, nothing fancy. *Thinner still*, she continues, *a face you would love to marry*. I'm told to stay perfectly still, to lift my head a little more, a little more, into the light. Strong bones are difficult to reenact. And like that, my brother's face emerges, out of nothing, flared up and finessed by the hands that've spent years developing this craft, hour after hour putting together the noses, the eyes, the lips that have gone silent. The same indifferent hands that'll one day take him out of this world for good. But my mother, concerned the face is not pale enough, stresses how he had her skin: delicate, stubborn. But it's late, too late. With a single loud clap, the officer brushes off whatever's left of my brother, a small cloud of ash rising from his hands before settling into the dust.

Los Muertos

He says he likes my tree, the way
its ink climbs my side. He hikes

up his pant leg, shines a flashlight
on his calf, a *Calavera* there—waves

of black hair and eyes like the center
of the Earth. *Oh!* I say. *You lost*

someone. He nods, pivoting his leg
on the barstool so I can see.

How did you know?
Two more *Calaveras*, little girls,

and I try to imagine
what that would do to a person,

shudder, order another round
of whatever he's buying.

The black-corseted bartender
takes me home. We have bad

sex. I find safety in sad things,
death spreading in a smile. I wake

to lost keys, call a cab, shiver
on my front stoop, that man's calf

on my mind as I shoulder
open the door.

from *The Porch Letters*

I am thankful
where many ferns are
How tough the black root-masses
covering stretches
pale and shaggy
leaning toward the sun without regret

How perfectly the wild poor ground
shelters cheerfulness
sodden drippings
cold mists

When I was a child
I learned how good a thing
shade is   The sound of it
The same note repeated
A secret nothing
Observing things that escape
strong long-sighted people

The Frog Pond

The house was built on granite. The granite reached beneath the water, under the seabed, beneath the mud and the clay. During low tide, pieces of it jutted up, penetrated the flat surface, creating slick, rocky paths out to sea.

Every August, they packed the car, filled it with books and clothes, their favorite sheets, Angela's chef ware and Martie's tennis equipment. Martie played tennis at the golf club. She played with Henry Arnold. Henry rented one of the island houses, but Martie and Angela always stayed at the house built on granite.

Driving up to Maine, Martie reflected on past summers, trying to recall as many details as she could, the Sundays wasted antiquing and the superfluous trinkets they acquired, that time they had discovered a school of porpoises while kayaking, the stretched-out day and how the sun sometimes hung in the sky, pausing before it dropped into night. They had been coming to Deer Isle for seven years, lengthening their stay from one week to two, to three. They now stayed on for the month of August.

Martie could have stayed longer. She enjoyed spending the long summer days with Angela and the way they revealed themselves to each other through the quiet daily rituals they created and adhered to, strictly, as if wavering from them would bring about catastrophe.

"Let's stop for lunch." Martie maneuvered the car into the right lane. Martie did not like others to drive. She felt agitated in the passenger's seat. Her eyes would dart left and right, as if careening off the road were only avoidable with her hands on the wheel.

After lunch they drove straight through for the remainder of the trip. Angela reached for Martie's hand as the car approached the steep, rickety causeway that passed between Deer Isle and the tip of land referred to as Little Deer Isle, where they would settle until summer's end.

The Realtors had left the key hidden for them outside the office. They always used the same hiding place and everyone in town knew of it. Martie let the car idle while Angela ran around the side, reached her hand into the azalea pot, and retrieved the key.

Angela smiled widely as she got back into the car, showing her off-colored, chipped tooth, the one with the half-dead root. Martie had asked Angela once how she got it, but she could not recall what Angela had said or if she had answered at all. Angela leaned over and kissed Martie's cheek and tickled her sides, jarring Martie from her thoughts. Martie giggled and swatted lightly at Angela's hands, breaking into a guffaw, one she could not rein in. The sound of it, Martie's cracked laugh, made Angela laugh too and they sat like that, with their backs against the seats, holding hands and giggling. "We're here." Martie pushed the car into drive. Angela let the cabin keys dangle from her hand and then pulled them in, closing them in her palm, against her chest.

The car skidded on the gravel when they pulled into the driveway. Martie eased the car to a stop. They left their bags and got out.

They stood facing the house. Martie looked off to the side, at the short walkway that connected the bathroom to the main house. Boring through the granite would destabilize the earth. Plumbing lines could not be run. The owners had installed an incinerator toilet, which burned their excrement. A waxy paper was inserted into the bowl, filled, and its contents dropped into the fire compartment beneath the toilet. A rusted foot pedal released the hatch. Martie liked to watch the flames lick the toilet basin; she liked the singe of the paper; she liked the idea of her waste being burned away. She saw it as an extension of her own biological process, her body's systematic breakdown of food, the digestive enzymes filtering the protein, the carbohydrates, the fat, the extraction of nutrients, the discarding of the rest.

Martie had majored in biology in college and had managed to cobble together a career as a medical writer. She'd met Angela when the New York office of *Psychology Today* hired her to edit an article that Angela had written about the effects of psych meds on prepubescent children.

"Sweetheart, come on." Angela had walked up to the door and was waiting for Martie to join her. Every summer they entered the house together, arm in arm, like newlyweds coming home for the first time. One year, Martie had tried to carry Angela through, but she'd overestimated her strength and both women had toppled in.

Inside, Martie spotted a puddle in the kitchen. There was always a problem with the house. The Realtor had called it "rustic" and had tried to sell them on a nicer place. Martie would have sprung for it, but Angela liked to fix things. She knew that it didn't matter to Angela that for all the money and effort spent on renovating the cabin they could have put a down payment on their own place. Each summer Angela would choose a project, necessary or not. Last year she had built shelves in the living room. She had measured out the length of the nook adjacent to the wood-burning stove and dragged Martie along to the lumberyard. Angela had asked her which cut of wood she liked best and then settled on one different from the one Martie had selected. She had purchased raw wood, stain, and sand paper.

Martie had watched her in the afternoons, standing over the planks that she had laid on the dining table. Using both hands, Angela brushed the sandpaper over the oak. She stretched across the wood in uniform strokes, pushing into a long stride. The muscles in her legs had tensed and bulged as she filed down the rough. Wood dust had sprinkled on the floor.

Now Martie stood back and watched Angela, who had climbed atop the kitchen counter and was running her hand over the ceiling. Tomorrow, she would drive to the hardware store to buy patching and other supplies needed to repair the leak. At least the owners give us a break on the rent, Martie thought.

"I'm playing tennis with Henry tomorrow," Martie said.

"What time?"

"Ten, I think. I'll have him pick me up."

Angela pulled her focus away from the leak and looked at Martie. "You hate how he drives."

"I can see you want to get started on the ceiling."

"Does it bother you?" Angela asked.

"I like to watch you work. It amazes me that you know how to fix things. Maybe one day you'll fix me."

"Stop, silly," she said and returned to inspecting the ceiling. Martie leaned her head to one side, looking up at her. She watched as Angela pressed her hand into the board. The plaster gave to her touch and when Angela removed her hand, Martie detected a faint, temporary impression of Angela's palm. "My mother was like you," Martie said. "Growing up, all the men on the block would call her when something went wrong with their houses. My father and I would stand over her toolbox, baffled, trying to figure out what tool she wanted. She'd roll her eyes and banish us."

Martie woke at six the next morning and went for a run. She started out east, downhill, through the town center and up the other side, through the winding hills to the Frog Pond. It had taken Angela and Martie five summers to learn about the lake. The Deer Isle community kept it a secret from outsiders. Martie remembered now that it was Henry who had told her about the lake, even though he'd just started coming to the isle two years ago, after his wife passed. Henry is like that, Martie thought, always linked in to the goings-on, despite his somewhat off-putting personality. He was loud and awkward, often interrupting conversations to make an inappropriate crack, but there was something childlike about him, and it was hard not to feel sympathy for the recent widower. Martie slowed to a walk, searching for the unmarked opening in the shrubbery that led to the water.

The lake shimmered under the sunrise, rippling slightly from the morning breeze. Martie had missed it here. She undressed, waded up to her midsection, and dove in. As she glided through the cold, she thought of how deep the lake must be. She had tried to find the bottom once, swimming downward until she lost her breath, then darting up and breaking the surface with a gasp.

She swam for only a few minutes before turning around. Her skin pimpled when she exited the water and she quickly put on her clothes. An animal in the brush startled her as she pulled her shirt over her head and she chuckled lightly to herself, remembering how it always took a few days to adjust from being in the city. There she could go anywhere, do anything, at any time. Here, in Deer Isle, it seemed as if everyone and everything was in sync with the moon's gravitational orbit. She walked back out to the road, rubbing her arms and legs, warming them, so as not to strain a muscle on the jog home.

When she reached the cabin, Angela was gone, already started on her project. Martie showered, listening to the water run out the open pipe, slap against the granite, and run off, finding its way to the patches of mud that lay in the creases between the rocks below. She heard the door rattle and ended her shower, wanting to kiss Angela before going off for the day. Martie grabbed a towel from the hook and opened the bathroom door.

"Oh god," Martie shouted. Droplets of water detoured around the bath towel and collected on the floor.

Henry Arnold grinned at her. "If we're late, they give our court away."

"You startled me, Henry."

"How was the drive up?"

"Let me put some clothes on," Martie said, wanting Henry to give her privacy, but he just stood there, staring at her, intending to keep up the conversation.

Angela walked in, looked at Martie frozen there, listening to Henry's chatter, unable to extract herself. "Henry, help me with the things in the car," she said.

❊ ❊ ❊

They were playing doubles with John and Barb Stanton. John had a powerful serve, while Barb's strength was placement. She was considered the most accurate player at the club. Together they presented a nearly undefeatable front, but Henry was scrappy and quick and hated to lose. Martie was out of practice but had an almost psychic instinct for where her opponents would play the ball. She could predict three to four volleys ahead. It was only when she lost her balance or when the game moved too fast that anything got by her. It infuriated Martie to see what was coming and not be able to do anything about it.

On the ride home Henry swerved across lanes to avoid potholes. "Been out to the lake yet?"

Martie averted her eyes to the oncoming traffic. She knew Henry was pissed that they'd lost. "This morning. How'd you know?"

"Cold?"

"Like a meat locker."

"Why don't you and Angela come for dinner Saturday? Susan and Glen are coming. And Bob and Dawn Ward from the inn."

"You sure about that, Henry? The Wards have never warmed up to me and Angela."

"Really? They've never said anything to me." Martie was annoyed at Henry's sudden diplomacy. She remembered back to last summer. There had been a commitment ceremony at Dawn's inn. She had heard Dawn in the restroom, talking to another woman, side by side, stall to stall.

"Well, Bob and I weren't sure. Two women—it's just not normal. But we needed the money and it sure does make for good party conversation." Martie heard the toilet flush and Dawn's abrupt, mirthless cackle. She darted out the door before anyone realized that she was there.

Martie turned to Henry. "What about you? No date?"

"The old birds up here?" Henry deliberately slowed his driving. Martie watched him; he seemed to look off, far ahead, down the road.

"I'm sorry, Henry. I didn't mean to push. I never even asked you about your wife. Was she sick? It must be difficult."

"It was sudden. I'm glad for that, but the shock of it has stayed with me." Henry skidded on the gravel and the car angled. Barely missed that tree, Martie thought. She grabbed her racket from the back and said goodbye. "All right. See you Saturday then. High tide's at 7:10 so come before."

Henry's place was located on one of the islets just off the main coast. At low tide one could walk out over the rocks, the seawater sunken, surrounding in the near distance. At high tide the ocean washed over the path and one could only return by boat. Martie recalled getting stranded at Henry's place on more than one occasion last summer.

Martie stood in the doorway and gazed into the living room. Angela sat in the window reading, the afternoon light draping over her. It soaked into the dark wood of the cabin and created a romantic, almost antique, candescence. Martie rested in the sight of her lover. Every year Angela read *A Room with a View*.

Angela looked up. "How was your match, honey?"

"We lost. Henry's irate. I thought he'd kill us on the drive back." Angela set down her book. Martie glanced at it. "*The Great Gatsby*? What happened to Forster? Did you two split up?"

"I've read it a dozen times."

"At least."

"I thought I'd try something new. Well, something old but different."

Martie had tried reading the Forster book two summers ago. She stopped halfway through it. She preferred contemporary work. Past was past. But Angela liked to excavate, and Martie admired her determination to discover something new in the book every year. Angela is like that, Martie thought, always set on making a situation work.

"Angela," Martie asked, "what happened to your tooth?"

"Schoolyard scuffle," she said. Martie knew there was more. Angela shrugged. "I didn't exactly read as normal in my Catholic high school. I should have gotten it fixed but never bothered."

Martie wasn't sure what more to say. "I bought oysters," she said.

In the evening, Martie and Angela sat near the wood-burning stove. They kept the door of it open, let its burnt embers light the room. With gloved hands, Martie grabbed a mollusk, drove the oyster knife in, twisted it and steadied the shell as the seal of it popped open. She handed it to Angela, careful not to spill the juice.

Angela tilted back her head, let the raw fish slide down her throat. Her thin frame in the firelight cast a long shadow onto the wall behind her. Martie had purchased two dozen. She opened and passed them to Angela in singles and watched as Angela devoured them. Angela loved oysters; Martie was allergic.

When the bowl was empty, Angela got up, washed her hands and brushed her teeth. She returned to the table, ripped bread from the loaf and spread cheese over it. She held it up to Martie and fed her from her hand. Angela filled their wine glasses. The women sipped at the Riesling that Martie had bought to go with the oysters. The cold, sweet liquid felt good in Martie's mouth, refreshing against the heat of the fire. Martie ran her hands along Angela's torso and kissed the length of her neck and the exposed skin of her shoulders. She felt Angela's muscles release.

At home, Angela could not shut off her phone or put down her reading. She'd view articles online late into the night, not getting to bed until two or three in the morning. Here, in Deer Isle, without the stress of her patients, Martie knew Angela could relax.

❊ ❊ ❊

On Saturday, Martie and Angela drove back to the Yacht Club, parked there and made their way to Henry's for dinner. Angela put two flashlights in her bag for the way back. She disliked walking over the rocks at night. Martie was surefooted and reveled in the challenge of it. Maybe they could leave before the tide went out and borrow Henry's boat. Navigating the shallow at night was probably more precarious than walking.

Martie stepped cautiously over the rocks, balancing a pie in one hand and a bottle of wine in the other.

When they arrived at the cottage, an escaped lobster had cornered Dawn Ward in the kitchen. "Get it!" she screamed. Martie hesitated. She could see sweat beads on Dawn's forehead. They were running down her face and streaking her makeup. Martie used a potholder and grabbed the lobster by its middle. It thrashed about in her hand, trying to nip her with its claws. She put it back in the fridge and closed the door.

"You won't see it again until it's on your plate."

"As it should be." Dawn skittered past Martie. "It's nice to see you."

Martie waited for Dawn to leave, opened up the fridge and winked at the lobster. Angela came up behind her, pressed her hands into Martie's shoulders. "I hear you're a hero."

"I was just talking to the culprit."

Angela pecked Martie's lips. "I can write you a prescription for that. Come on, lobster whisperer. Let's go inside."

Martie and Angela sat down around the dining table. It took up most of the room and its thick stumps had started to warp from the condensation. Martie felt trapped there, wedged between the wood and the wall. She fidgeted, uncomfortable, crossing her legs left and right. Everyone sat around, stuffing themselves with shrimp cocktail. Martie slid hers over to Angela, inconspicuously, not wanting to attract attention.

After the appetizer, Henry got up from the table. He removed the lobsters from the refrigerator and set them, one by one, on the stovetop. Martie watched from the dining table as he held a lobster up over the boiling pot. The frozen, near-dead fish, feeling the sudden heat on its claws, began to twitch frenetically in Henry's hand. Henry loosened his fingers and let the lobster drop into the pot. When the shell softened, he fished it out with salad tongs. In total there were seven lobsters, piled atop each other on a platter. Martie noted the limp claws hanging over the side of the dish as Henry passed the dinner table and walked out onto the deck. Martie felt a poke in her side. Angela had been elbowing her under the table. Martie had a tendency to get quiet in groups and

Angela wanted her to participate more. Martie smiled at everyone. "I'm going to keep the chef company," she said and excused herself from the table.

Outside the night was calm and starless. Martie listened for the sound of the tide but couldn't hear anything over Henry's racket. "Couldn't stand to be away from me, huh?" Henry said without looking up. Martie stood beside him and watched his hands working. Henry lifted a lobster, set it on a board and, with a long knife, cut through it, splitting the shell in two. He poured melted butter over the fish meat and set it on the grill. The flames kicked up. Martie listened to the fire snap. When he lined up all the lobsters, Henry took a frying pan lid and pressed it down against one of them. Martie could see the creature flatten; its soft white flesh sizzled and the heat released the aroma of fish and butter, a fragrance so rich that Martie thought she would vomit.

"I'm going back inside. All right, Henry?"

"The process is a little barbaric," he said, "but the results are delicious."

Once Henry finished grilling, the rest of the meal was brought out: linguine with clams, mushrooms stuffed with crabmeat, and corn. Martie nibbled quietly on an ear and got drunk on wine.

"Henry, do you have any plain pasta for Martie?" Angela said. She knew Martie would get emotional if she drank too much without food.

Dawn leaned in, stretching her neck as far over the center of the table as she could. "I noticed you weren't eating."

"She has a shellfish allergy."

"Oh, Jesus, Martie. I forgot. All of the pasta's covered in clams, but I might have some bread. Do you want it toasted?"

"Sure," Martie said. She felt everyone looking at her.

"How awful for you, Martie. It's so scrumptious."

"Thanks, Dawn, but I don't miss it." Martie spread butter over the charred squares that Henry had dropped on her plate.

"Now I bet that's a meal you'll be talking about for the rest of your life," Henry said, and everyone laughed.

"I'm fine, Henry. Don't worry about it."

"Has anyone tried the new restaurant in Blue Hill? I hear it's fantastic," Susan said.

"Overrated," Dawn said. "Bob and I tried it out last week."

"What's the most memorable meal you've ever had?" Glen asked, looking up, big-eyed with raised eyebrows. Martie liked Glen; he loved to eat.

"Well, honey, that's easy," Susan said. "The one where you proposed to me." She scanned the table. "He was such a romantic when he was younger."

Martie noticed the blush on Glen's face. She could feel her own cheeks getting hot. Martie chomped on her toast and swigged her wine.

"I would say our most memorable meal was in Paris. Wouldn't you agree, Bob?" Bob nodded, not looking up from his plate. "We had gone there for our honeymoon. It was called chez something or other. Bob, honey, do you remember the name? It's quite famous actually. I remember I ordered the coq au vin and Bob ordered the duck."

"We had snails," Bob said.

"Escargot, Bob. We had the escargot for an appetizer. After all, we were in France."

"My most memorable was Thanksgiving when I was twelve. My grandmother let me prepare the meal with her. I'd never tasted turkey so good as when I'd personally labored over it," Angela said.

"Angela is quite the cook," Henry said. "I'd have to say my best meal was at your cabin last summer. The sea bass with the roasted tomatoes—delicious."

"She makes an exquisite soufflé too," Martie said.

"That's sweet. You two make such a cute couple," Susan said.

Martie's face was flush and the whites of her eyes had turned red. "Angela has made my most favorite meals, but not my most memorable."

"Martie," Angela said.

"Well now we're all curious," Dawn said.

"My most memorable meal was at a barbecue. I was probably seven. My uncle Joe, who was no relation to me, threw a July 4th party at his place at the lake in the outskirts of town. Joe had no children of his own, but he liked kids and made up all sorts of games to play with his friends' children, thus the uncle title. I remember my parents had to leave early, but I whined. I wanted to stay longer. Stephanie Sweeney's parents offered to take me home." Martie hiccupped, dribbling wine on her chin. "Excuse me." She dabbed her face with a napkin. "Joe was grilling skewered meat. I remember Stephanie and me leaning against each other, watching Joe turn the skewers over the flames. He gave some meat to Stephanie and offered me some too. I took it. I ate it. I had never tasted chicken like it. The marinade had made it tender and juicy. When I'd eaten it all, Joe took me aside and told me it was rabbit. I threw up, but I never told my parents. It was a secret between Joe and me."

"Do you ever see Joe now?" Glen asked.

"No. He left town suddenly a couple of years later."

Angela stood from the table and squinted out the window. "I think the tide's going out."

❊ ❊ ❊

The ping of the hammer against the tiny shingle nails awakened Martie. She tried to ignore it. She could hear Angela prying broken shingles from the roof. They popped up and slid down, scraping against the other shingles and landing on the deck, teetering against the wood. Martie gave in to the noise, roused herself from the bed, put on running shorts and a t-shirt, and walked out onto the deck. "Getting an early start?" She wetted her finger and rubbed the corner of her eye.

"It's nearly eight. You never sleep this long. It was all that wine on an empty stomach."

"I had toast."

"You got drunk and told that story about that awful man," Angela said.

"Joe?"

"What prompted you to tell it?"

"Didn't Glen ask?" Martie tried to remember the conversation. "I don't know. It just came into my head. Because I was watching Henry grill, I guess."

"A grown man keeping secrets with kids — that's the kind of story that makes people talk, Martie."

"What? About what?" Martie could tell she had upset her.

"Never mind," Angela said. "Drink some water before you run. It's already sweltering." Martie could feel the sun on the top of her head. She went back inside and put on a cap.

It was Sunday and the town was quiet. None of the stores opened before noon. She ran along the pier. The sun was still red in the sky, and she remembered her grandmother, her father's mother, who would vacation with them sometimes at the Jersey Shore when Martie was a girl, and she remembered her grandmother rustling her out of bed in the morning to watch the sunrise and how the fiery orb burnished the azure, and she remembered her grandmother gazing upon it and rubbing her hand tenderly against Martie's back and pointing with her other hand up into the sky and quoting a wives' tale, "red sun in the morning sailor's warning," and Martie remembered how her grandmother's sing-song delivery of the foreboding news frightened her, and she felt the same chill stream through her body as she had felt as a girl, and Martie stopped running for a moment and stood, breathy and sweaty. She stared at the sun slicing through the horizon, and she wondered if her grandmother's prediction were true, if there would be a storm tonight. The black, still ocean gave no indication.

She filled her lungs and started up again, running through town and up into the hills. She could feel the skin on her arms and on the backs of her legs burning from the sun. A cramp in her side distracted her. She had lost her rhythm when she stopped. She took deep breaths in and expelled all the air from her lungs and belly, trying to allay the pain. She continued with the discomfort for another mile before deciding to walk it out. The heat was overbearing anyway; she'd go to the Frog Pond for a swim.

Martie noted the change in temperature when she stepped onto the shaded trail and how it cooled as she descended the modest slope to the lake. She sat a while on a rock, listening to the dragonflies winging through the air and to the courting calls of the frogs, the same amphibian croak that had inspired the lake's name. She closed her eyes and let nature's cacophony wash over her. From somewhere far off she heard the cry of a rooster, and it startled her. It must be from the Wards' inn, she thought, recalling that they kept chickens in their barn.

Martie dove under and resurfaced coughing. The drastic temperature change shocked her body, and she felt as though her heart stopped for a moment, and she thought she might cry, and then she thought herself foolish for responding so histrionically to a little cold water.

She began swimming with elongated strokes. She imagined her arms and legs stretching out far in front and behind her body, leaving a rolling wake in her path. She thought of Angela's limbs, envisioned them moving through the water, faster and more powerful than Martie's squat arms and legs. She thought about the dinner at Henry's and the morning with Angela. Why had the story about Joe upset her? Sometimes Angela acted as if she knew things about her that Martie didn't know herself. It was the most annoying thing about being with an analyst. Sometimes Martie felt like a kid being observed by her mother. Martie picked up her pace. She hadn't realized she was mad at Angela.

About a half-mile out, a weeping willow grew aslant, leaning over the lake. Martie had picked it as her marker. When she reached the tree, she rested, treading water, calm and methodical, trying to regain her breath. She lay back and floated atop the water. The sun warmed her front, while the frigid water held her up. She closed her eyes and relaxed.

A fish grazed at Martie's fingers, and she screamed loudly. The open air absorbed the sound, reduced it to a peep.

She sank back into the water, treading, readying herself to swim back. The fish nibbled at her again, this time at her leg. Martie examined the water and saw a flash of white bobbing below her. It must be an overgrown water plant, she thought, and dunked under, grabbing at it.

She caught hold of it and felt soggy, bloated flesh. Martie pulled. A young girl's body sprang toward her. The girl's head briefly cracked the water's surface. The skin on her face had started to corrode, but the girl's eyes glistened. The sight of it sent terror through Martie and she could make no sound. She let go. The girl bobbed before her, obstructing Martie's path, seeming to mock her. Martie had to swim around. She felt her strokes, short and chaotic, and her breath, broken. She gasped but could not get enough air. Martie sprang from the water. Her clothes were in a heap and difficult to put on. She felt them cling to her wet skin. Martie ran up to the road and stood on the pavement, waving her arms at passersby. "Why is no one stopping!" she said out loud and pulled her tangled hair away from her eyes. Finally, a maroon sedan slowed and stopped at the side of the road. It was Dawn Ward. "Get in, Martie. Get in!" Dawn shouted at her, but Martie just stood there. Her legs had stiffened and they felt like stone. Dawn reached over, took Martie by the hand and pulled her into the car. They drove to the police station where Martie made the report.

❊ ❊ ❊

Angela was sitting on the porch when Martie drove up with Dawn. Angela waved and watched Dawn back out, the tires of her car spinning on the gravel.

"Was that Dawn Ward?" Angela said. "You should have invited her in."

"I—," Martie said and trailed off.

"What's wrong, Martie?" Angela embraced her and led her inside.

❊ ❊ ❊

Two days later, someone left the local paper on Martie and Angela's front porch. They hadn't ordered it. Martie found it there early that morning, before Angela woke up. Martie sat down on the steps, the dew-covered wood against her legs, chilling her. She read the words, filing away the information as if it had been another person. Even reading her own name, it had seemed like a stranger who had discovered the girl's body. The girl was found and dragged out from the lake. The cold water had helped to preserve her body, but bits of her flesh were gone. The fish had fed upon her. A mark ran around the girl's left ankle, like some sort of burn, like someone had affixed something to her, trying to weight her body. The initial report estimated that the girl had been dead three weeks. The girl had been violated, the article said. Martie closed and folded the paper. She couldn't read anymore. She carried it into the bathroom. She dropped a piece of wax paper into the toilet and set the newspaper inside it. Martie set her foot on the rusted pedal and pushed. She felt its resistance and the strain of her calf muscle. She pressed harder. The hatch opened and the flames leapt up, setting fire to the article. Martie watched it burn down, watched the pages shrivel into ash. She watched until it was small enough to fit through the hole in the toilet basin, and then she watched it slip through the hole and fall into the fire compartment. She walked back into the bedroom and lay beside Angela, watching her sleep.

❊ ❊ ❊

Martie and Angela returned to their routine. In the mornings Martie jogged, though she never went back to the lake. Angela rose with her and worked on the roof. She'd been at it for two weeks and still had not located the source of the leak. It was late afternoon on a Thursday. A couple of police officers showed up. "We have some follow-up questions," they said. They sat on the deck. The smell of fish hung in the air. Low tide. The sun burned Martie's face. She squinted.

"Had you been at the lake on prior occasions?"

"I think I'd been out three times this season. I sometimes swim after my morning run."

"Had you noticed anything suspicious?"

"Nothing out of the ordinary." Martie was quiet. "It gives me the chills to think she had been there all that time. What if another child had found her?"

Martie watched as Henry walked onto the deck. "Henry Arnold." He shook the cops' hands.

"We're playing tennis at the club," Martie said and felt ridiculous. These men were trying to solve a murder.

"You're working on the drowning? Were you able to I.D. the girl?" Henry said.

"Yes. Her family has been contacted." The cop shifted his glance between Martie and Henry. "We'll just be a few more minutes, if you could please wait inside." Henry hesitated. It's as if he's never been asked to leave a room before, Martie thought.

Martie played badly that day. Her placement was poor and she slugged across the court, her sneakers landing heavily on the asphalt. Henry pouted and yelled at Martie during the match, but after they lost, Henry exhibited uncharacteristic compassion. "Your mind's on other things. I can tell," he said.

Martie didn't hear him. She was looking up. The sky had turned a dark purple and the clouds whirled around it, creating a shifting palette of shapes.

"Look, Henry," Martie said. "The sky."

Henry raked his neck upward. "I've never seen anything like it."

"It looks like the world is ending." She turned her eyes from it and faced Henry. "Like in that book with the chicken. Like the sky is falling."

❀ ❀ ❀

Martie dropped Henry at the Yacht Club. She waited, watching him free the dinghy from the dock, untying the braided rope, freshly bought. Bits of the old knot, cut and starting to fray, had been pushed aside to accommodate the new rope. He boarded the dinghy, leaning forward and pulling the oars with ease. The little boat shot through the water. Henry was fifteen years older than Martie, but he was strong. Martie had noted it on the tennis court and looked on him now, held in the dichotomy of his body, of the bald, wrinkled top attached to the muscular torso. He was powerful, Martie thought. She remembered once they had played the Andersons. Mrs. Anderson was the eldest member of the club, still playing at eighty-eight. Henry took no pity. When it came his turn to serve, he shifted his weight back, exaggerated, as if he was trying to wind up. He torpedoed the ball at Mrs. Anderson, hitting her in the face and knocking her down. Henry jumped the net, checking to see that she was all right, but his behavior had shocked Martie. He then went on to make such an ordeal, apologizing to Mrs. Anderson and proclaiming how badly he felt, that other members of the club came over to make sure Henry was okay instead of Mrs. Anderson, who was sitting on the sideline with ice on her cheek.

On the way home Martie stopped to buy oysters. Joan Cummings, the owner of the shop, stood behind the counter. One of the kids they hired to cover must have called in sick, Martie thought.

"Hi, Joan." Joan did not look up. Martie waited. Maybe she was counting. Or maybe she didn't hear her. "Joan, how are you?"

"Can I help you?" she said, not making eye contact.

"Joan? Martie. Martie Bernstein."

"I know. I was just talking with Dawn. You know Dawn

Ward from the inn. She picked you up that day. The day you reported the drowning. Seeing a thing like that—I wouldn't be able to leave the house."

"I can't imagine what it must be like for the girl's family."

"The paper said she was in the fetal position when they drug her out." It wasn't true, but Martie didn't correct her. "What kind of a perverse person would violate a seven-year-old girl? Not anyone normal, that's for sure." Joan adjusted her head and looked at Martie.

"I'm just picking up some oysters. For Angela."

"Dawn said you don't eat shellfish."

There was a pause. "There are some very sick people out there," Martie said.

"How many?" Martie looked at Joan, confused.

"Oh. Two dozen. Six of each kind." Joan shoveled them into a bag and handed it to Martie. "Don't you usually separate the different types?"

"No." Joan rang her up and Martie left. The outside of the bag dripped with salt and grime. Martie set it down on the car floor and drove home.

Joan had always sorted the different oysters into different bags. Martie was certain of it. She recalled discussing the range of tastes with Angela. In some parts of the country the oysters were cleaned before serving. Angela disliked these. She loved the gritty, fishy oysters of the Northeast. She'd often scrape the shell with her teeth, dislodging the oyster's foot. She'd always do this when she was alone with Martie and would often do it in public, even though it was considered gauche. Martie liked to watch Angela pull at the meaty fish with her teeth; it was primal, so unlike Angela's typical, cerebral way.

She parked at the far end of the drive and approached the cabin. The house rested on stilts, the thick wooden squares wedged in between the granite. If the rocks shifted, it seemed to Martie, the whole house would collapse and splinter against the gray and yellow stone.

She opened the door. Angela stood in the kitchen, scoring shingles with a utility knife. Martie could see that she'd been working for some time. Damaged shingles piled up at the other end of the table.

"Looks like progress," Martie said.

"I can't find the leak. I'm replacing everything that's broken."

"Why don't we just tell the owners they need to hire a roofer?"

Angela looked up from her work. Her eyes were bloodshot. "It might be in one of the angles or in the flashing around the gas vent. I saw rust spots." Angela broke off the end of a shingle. It fell to the ceramic floor and cracked. She slammed her palm against the table. "They used nails of a different metal."

"I don't understand," Martie said. She'd never seen Angela distraught over a repair.

"It's galvanized rust. Chemical erosion. From the different alloys pressing against each other."

The bag of oysters swayed in Martie's hand; the slime and plastic hit against her leg. She felt her skin begin to itch and looked at it and then at Angela.

"They're all mixed together," Angela said.

"I know. Joan packed them that way. I said something, but she behaved strangely today."

"How?"

Martie shrugged. "I don't know. Like I'd done something wrong. Like she was angry with me about something."

"Maybe she was having an off day."

"Angela, I was thinking maybe we could go home."

Angela surveyed the room. Shingles lay on the floor and table. "When? I can't just leave in the middle."

"I keep seeing her. Her eyes. It was like she was still alive."

"Things happen that we have no control of. You have to accept that. I understand if you want to go, but you've always loved it here. We've spent years settling into this community."

"Did you see the sky today?" Martie turned to walk away.

"You run from everything, Martie. What will people think if we leave?"

"Why do you care? You think Dawn Ward's opinion or Henry's matters? They're just small people in a big world."

"Did something happen with Henry?" Angela said.

"I'm just fed up."

"Jesus, honey. Your leg's all red."

"What?" Martie looked down. Her skin was swollen and bumpy. "Goddamn shellfish!" She threw the bag across the kitchen. It hit the far wall and slid down. The oysters spilled out.

Martie looked at the black shells spread across the floor. "Sorry," she said.

"I'll clean it," Angela said. "You better wash your leg."

❄ ❄ ❄

Martie turned on the shower and stepped in. She lathered her leg with soap, making sure to wash away the fish oil. It had gotten into her pores. She began to feel relief, the hives subsiding. She put her head under, closing her eyes and letting the water run over her body. She wished the whole thing could be washed away.

Martie breathed deeply. A neighbor was barbecuing and the smoke had wafted over, through the open window in the bathroom. The scent of it entered Martie's nostrils and she began to cry.

"Joe," she said aloud. Her body shook.

Martie wasn't supposed to have seen it, but when Joe saw her there, he had encouraged Martie to watch. Stephanie's underpants lay on the ground, next to Stephanie's sandaled feet. The white lace of the ribbing was torn and covered in dirt. Martie fixed her eyes on them, except for that one moment when she'd caught Stephanie's stare. She was looking out, looking at nothing. Martie should have run for help.

After, Joe fed them the rabbit meat, and Martie threw up. Joe told them it was a secret, as if the thing that was bad was the rabbit.

❄ ❄ ❄

Martie dressed and went to find Angela. She saw that Angela had cleaned everything and had set a small table near the wood-burning stove. She had put out candles, and a bottle of champagne was chilling in a cleaned-out tomato can they'd used the week before. Angela walked in, carrying a bunch of wildflowers she had picked along the road out front.

"How's your leg?" Angela asked. Martie just nodded. "I made you steak. I figured you need protein after the day you've had." She'd been the one barbecuing. Angela held her hand out to her, beckoning Martie to sit beside her and eat. Martie poked at the steak with a fork. It was rare and the juice ran out from it, covering the plate. Martie looked away.

"What's wrong?" Angela said.

"I feel like everything we built here is being threatened."

Angela took Martie's hands. "Of course you do," she said. "That's normal after what you've been through. But we've got a good foundation." Angela nodded assuredly and Martie nodded in response.

"There's more," Martie said.

Outside the cloud cover had moved in over the house, and the sky had turned dark. Martie saw lightning flash. In seconds a boom shook the house and rain cascaded from the sky in tiny, dart-like drops that chinked against the granite and beat on the deck and roof. Angela and Martie watched as one piece of the ceiling caved and fell onto the kitchen floor. Water poured in, bringing bits of shingle and twigs from the outside. Martie jumped to her feet and ran over, trying to catch some of the water with a garbage pail, but it was useless. The water soaked her, and within seconds she was covered with scraps of debris. The wind swept through the hole in the roof. Martie ran back to Angela and huddled against her, shivering. There was nothing Martie could do to stop it.

Ashley Inguanta, photograph

Soft

Everything was soft
upon the wet sand:

Our ship.
Our footprints.
Your tools.
Our bags.

We carried things out from the creaking
hulls

while each wave
split more of their skin—

How was I to know that soft foam
was as sharp as teeth?

Sections of hulls already
washed away,

pieces left alone

beached whales,

                        slabs of white wood,

offerings.

The Chiffon Game

St. Thomas, December 2011

The object is to watch
my mother lose the scarf
women in our family
have been wearing for decades.
Slipping through the barren
knot of a cavern, rising as
a question, no clutch strong enough
to stop the Loa I read about
from stealing what He believes
is rightfully His. My mother's neck
reddens with concern when I tell her
I will write a poem about this
because she knows it will involve
more than chiffon. Within, it will contain
the most careful references to a boy
I passed on this beach, his mouth tight
as a sea star, skin more tempting
than the Loa's. A boy who would slip
into a cave, find a scarf and wear
the cloth as a sunset across his own neck.

Craigslist Post Id: 5339677111 Explains

Because of how the minutes pull apart
into breathless seconds as I listen

so close I can hear the sky move over
top—straining for car door and footstep; heart

beat so fast, my breath in short gasps, my skin
prickled with goosebumps though the furnace blows

—the dim room's less empty filled with dry heat—
while the moonlight creeps inside through the blinds;

and the house itself seems to hold its breath,
the doors stand still, the walls at parade rest

and even the ice in the freezer grips
itself from shifting, while we all wait taut

as tripwires, stretched strings, rigged to explode
—is why I don't ask, need, or want your name.

Linnaeus at the Window

This kind of snow I think is called *powder*
which means dry and new and isn't called *firn*

which is older than a year—it's more fresh
than that, newer too than the young snow called

névé which melts a bit then refreezes,
the kind you find helping to form glaciers—

this is not the first snow this cold winter
just the first carried in on such fast wind—

this fierce storm's a real whiteout, called *snow squall*,
born of the nor'easter circling the last

six hours off the coast counter-clockwise.
The nurses tsk-tsk when I ask, *tell me*

the difference between HIV and AIDS,
as if they're afraid of what comes with a name.

Naming the Plants

Unbroken ocean of green. Nothing
for the eye to rest on. Everything
the same, as far as the eye
could see. Farther.

    Indian Bread Root, Yellow Star Grass, Golden Alexander,
    Seneca Root, Prairie Cordgrass, Prairie Dropseed, Big Bluestem

Look closely—the flowers
and grasses are not alike. We
would do well to give them names,
as Adam gave the animals

       And out of the ground the Lord God formed every beast of the
       field, and every fowl of the air; and brought them unto Adam to
       see what he would call them: and whatsoever Adam called every
       living creature, that was the name thereof.

    Prairie Crocus, Prairie Smoke, Smooth Fleabane, Black-eyed Susan,
    Yellow Coneflower, Meadow Blazing Star, Low Prairie Rose

And what of the woman
we stayed with our first summer?
I taught her to plait her hair
like mine, to throw off her blanket
and wear a proper dress.

    Nodding Ladies Tresses, Small White Ladyslipper

She cared for the baby while we worked our wheat,
built a bridge from willow twigs
to ford our little stream. She
was a good Indian. No, I don't recall that she had
a name. I did not record it.

Thimble

Chilocco Indian School, 1898

at first it felt clumsy
like I had grown two
extra fingers

hand stitching
the way my mother taught me
weaving the needle in and out
in a straight line
was no longer possible

In the first year: Never permit sewing without a thimble

and I couldn't figure out what to do
with my fingers
could not make them curl
just so like a lady's hands

my hands are wide like my father's
and so are my fingers

Do not let children make knots in thread.

with no knot, my thread kept slipping out
of the needle

it was like learning to sew
all over again

All civilized nations have obtained their culture through the work of the hand assisting the development of the brain.

putting on a thimble hurts

it needs to be snug
to trap the fingers

Basketry, weaving, netting, and sewing were the steps in culture taken by primitive people.

not so tight that you need to force it on
but tight enough so it doesn't slip off
by itself

Biting threads must never be tolerated.

my thread shreds so fast

Drill in the use of the thimble, length of the thread, threading needle, motion of arm in taking stitches, fastening thread

the proper hold takes a while to get used to

we make dishtowels and pillowcases by the hundreds
practical things to be used at the school
patch and darn day after day
sew silver buttons
on pinafores and uniforms

Drill in the use of emery and holding scissors

the teachers believe we will stab ourselves
without the use of a thimble
they do not want our stain
on their needlework

Text in italics is from the Uniform Course of Study prescribed by Estelle Reel, Superintendent of Indian Schools, 1898-1910.

Hanging Tree

Now that she has made up her mind,
a calm descends. The peace that passeth
all understanding. Don't think about God.
After the clothes are shaken out, the last
of the cabbage made into soup, what
is there left to look at? A table, two chairs
and a bed.

To walk five miles at a quickish pace
on a groomed trail without a break
(and wearing good shoes) would take
about a hundred minutes. This is not
that walk. The ground slick
with hoppers. Smoke rising from the fields
where the fools tried to catch them in pans
of burning oil. The tatters of what used to be
her garden. The patched, shabby boots.

She stops to rest awhile and the irony
is not lost on her. If you had a tree
on the horizon you could judge the passing
of time but she has no tree, just time.

In the high rocky hills, she knows she could find
pine. Below that, burr oak, green ash,
white elm. On lower ground, linden
or basswood, any number of willows:
peach-leaf, river-bank, slender or diamond.
In the deep cool ravines, balsam poplar
or the paper birch. For gullies, not much
but scrub cedar.

She walks on, scans the flat horizon. Down to the river,
down to the water, down to where the trees
are sure to grow strong enough. Cottonwoods shake
their hair out over the muddy trickle below.

For a loop, the hem around her skirt will likely do.
A tear started along the seam should make easy work
of that. Still, it must be strong enough to hold her weight,
which is now a good deal less than it is about to become.
She likes to take care of things. She likes to get things done.

Ashley Inguanta, photograph

We Return to Ritual

to the graveyard we hunted
    as girls
spreading paper rolls
    across the stones
like sheets over corpses
    rubbing thick chalk back
and forth to raise
    words from the dead

the ritual was in the reveal
    we held our breaths
while letters became faces
    numbers became bodies
we pressed paper to muddy earth
    waiting to feel

more than ourselves we
    were so close

Stella Dallas

Anne Shirley, who plays the daughter,
grew up on the RKO lot,
graduated from the studio high school.
For her eighteenth birthday,
Goldwyn gave her a car.
Hollywood was her every day.
She'd put in her shift on the soundstage,
then go home and cry because
the director would not direct her.
In *Stella Dallas* the daughter marries money.
Even though we know real life
is always about the young and sexy,
this movie is all about the mother.

Bird-breasted and built for speed,
Stanwyck wore three sets of stockings
in order to have thick ankles. She said,
"It was a matter of upholstery."
She stuffed cotton in her cheeks for jowls.
My poor old mom took it on the chin.
My dad dropped her when his first love
got divorced. My sister remembers
more than I: how our stepmother
walked the hall on Sunday mornings,
saying, your mother is a whore,
saying, you will all wind up in hell.
My sister says she's buried now
in my father's hometown, that hag.

Anne Shirley played the younger Stanwyck
in *So Big*. If the daughter is the mother,
is she a premonition or nostalgia?
My sister's middle name is Anne,
in honor of our mother's mother.
Really, I have just a handful of memories.
The burgers at the café in Underwood
where my father took us. My sister

remembers the name of the place. I just
remember the taste of too much pepper.
Or walking my father's farm after school,
finding cactus growing in a streambed.
Chasing the planter behind my father's tractor.
My sister says it's time to let that handful go
because it all comes down to dirt.

They say Stanwyck came from nothing,
even though her family dates back to 1740.
Her father left them to work on the Panama Canal
after her mother died. Her sister raised her.
Stanwyck's husband, Robert Taylor,
was born in a small town in Nebraska,
just like my father. During the making
of all those movies we love her for,
Stanwyck was suing the studios to get paid,
angry and grief-stricken at the loss of her sister.
In both the silent and the sound
versions of *Stella Dallas,* at the end
the camera closes up on the mother
crying at the fence, as the story
struggles to make sense.

Café Imagination

If we choose marriage let our minds
pledge comradeship at the image
nation's altar, let the magi officiate

from their painted frames: Wynton
Marsalis and Louis Armstrong cheek-
puff and horn against tuba bricks.

Let my vows cite the way you write
vowels *oh oh* for *uh oh* and that you
call sprinkles sparkles. Let each vow

end like a dark berry at the window
a sky sentence period or a dried bud
on the pavement its tentacles a tiny

squid all dry and desiccated, a sock,
a bottle, last leaves of the year. Let
me bare the way I mistook a mural

for a bird flock when the winged
gashes were just exposed concrete
patches where the paint rubbed off.

Let our bands be part Biosphere snow
village carved from the fur-covered
ice blocks and beds, a trumpet frozen

in the igloo wall, the glint of the ice
chapel's altar; and part Biodome home
with the botanical garden's Chinese

lantern glow as alien as the Olympic
stadium rocket ship dock or the red
tendon roller coaster loops, the green

wind, the scraps of indigo lit French.
And for honeymoon let us venture
pigment brush to sand dunes, storks

horses in a field, lighthouse shore
scene on the Riviera elephants, koi
under lilypad hawk in a tree deer

silhouetted on the plains Chinese
girl portrait at once both empress
and peasant your Coney Island

prints. A toast then over my chai
and your coffee all smiles as we sit
nestled in these red pleather arms:

let no one tell us how to be gay
and like Polaris let what I have
name-splayed here today bride us.

Proof of Intent to Marry

DOMA fell and I began the hard
sell for you to move here life
there no longer the heart knock

you once heard. So it was form
this and fee that and statement
of intent signed and cosigned

or is that sine and cosine? Divide
the length of you by me and find
a tangent : where and when did

we meet and how three functions
to avoid the same idea of why
two would choose to dissolve

the border reduce the right angle
to map the erotography of us
the tale of us transformed into

a table of visits, dates and six
years of you are here and I am
there and for how many days

and here's your train ticket
and here's my boarding pass
and does any other relationship

bear this level of calculation?
And wait, it's not enough?
Homeland Security requires

more evidence? Here's a letter
here are three more. No
no announcement went out

and how can one set a date
in the neverending wait. Queer
or straight you assume

tradition and isn't that the debate?
We'll kill white gowns and cakes?
So our clerk's office intent

and my financial records
the Debeers receipt for our bands
and like their hidden diamond

chips you're approved. There are
packets and a physical, blood
tests and an interview and a new

name, beneficiary, fiancé say
one thing about me that you can
not stand and wouldn't I like

to know and you are Visa and you
are welcome to the US of A
and in June you will move here

your neighbor will practice the violin
achromatic scales as we pack,
the Garmin's first words will be turn

right on Avenue Des Pen Ees
and what will the border agent say
during those longest sunlit hours

will we wed the same day a supreme
courting weighs yay or nay to what
is already true in both arc and rhyme

Q X 4: *an excess*

1

Quinine in the tonic maybe. That side-taste in which something
brushes the tongue like suede or butter. We drank a lot of it near the
equator. Otherwise the mosquitos were deadly, cruising, half Q-tip,
half dentist drill. Cumulatively they might take a whole bloodstream
off into the air. They're all female the ones we swat and spatter. Stay
very still. They read us for heat, not for money, not even for IQ. Some
of us stink a little better. Some of us like gin on the rocks.

2

Once you sit in one of the classroom chairs, you'll see why it's
difficult being querulous here. Everything is stiff and will not let you
get up easily once you've slid into the seat and put your elbows on
the desks. My third grade teacher was a kind of quarrel unto herself.
When she didn't like you, she'd hit you in the back of the head. Everyone grew quiet. I avoided all her violence by learning how to perfectly
replicate the cursive letters in the worksheets she assigned us. When
she asked me to show the class what a perfect assignment looked like,
I jumped up proudly and walked among my classmates proudly. How
odd that the capital Q in cursive looked so much like a complicated 2.

3

Better when the letter's inside the word. Equipment. Equal. Antique.
Better not to start something you can't quit. Quibble all you want but
that won't end it. Nothing ends the same where it begins. In this way
it resembles a kind of aesthetic of the unresolved circle, the struck-out
whole, the balloon with a pin in it the millisecond before it bursts in
your hands.

4

Quartz remembers, they say, its handling. Quirks in the electrical field
return to normal. Whatever the quality that makes them so impres-
sionable, certain of us remain skeptical. But there they are among the
grains and shells and snails absorbing the sea. We grow queasy at the
end of so much looking for a mouth in the midst of all that whispering.
Better to stick it on a necklace or a ring, where it might quietly keep
us from exploding.

Thesaurus

By then, nearly everyone had gone: her parents
of course, the sister who died young, her brothers
years ago. Her husband survived double broken legs
but not the cigarettes. Eventually, her remaining sister
passed and the house had to be sold. Her hips quit
and even language deserted her. Dad and I brought her
peonies to smell, chocolate mints to taste,
and tried to translate the strange dialect she had acquired
from the stroke. But the clearest sentiments
she uttered were those gusty sighs — so sour
in the air between us, I wondered who
helped her brush her teeth and soak her dentures.
That's when she took my hand in the suede
of hers. The turquoise skin
draped from her knuckles as if something
inside her had escaped, like helium
from last weekend's carnival balloon.
Yes: touch. But the hell of it was
I could hear her, as if that were the last open channel
through the surrounding static
and my body's chance to convey
all the things we want to say at the end
but for which we have no words.
And maybe she was listening.
I wish now I had taken all the ugly names
I was calling myself in those days and nailed them
to the wall, sat down with her to see
if *sick* and *fag* and *loser* stuck.
Or if they slid to the floor on their own viscous trails.
That is, if she could see them at all,
what with her left eye blind, the right
looking for a door, and her hands busy
calling me out from the warren of my heart.

Powers

On the playground, he lays
his small body on concrete
to carefully trace his form
in chalk. First the feet,
then the legs. Up one side
and down the other. Outlines
each contour, and copies
himself in friction and dust.

Like the Invisible Woman
who wills herself to vanish.
Becomes an ivory shadow
amid comic-book crimson
and turquoise. Her dotted line
here, and not here, simultaneously.
Transparent enough to slip
from panel to panel. To evade

red dodgeballs aimed his way,
he practices a fade on the sidelines.
The boys fire away, so he teaches himself
to be faint. To empty himself
of his self.
        When he goes home
to the question, *How was school?*, empty
white speech balloons swarm the air.

Writing in Women's Bars

Tonight it is June who says, "I want to dance with you." It is June who leads me, she heavy and I light and willowy. . . . The men, in stiff evening shirts, stiffen even more in their chairs. The women close their lips tightly. . . . The men feel insulted. At the table a waiter is waiting to tell us we cannot dance again. Then I call for the bill like a grand seigneur and we leave. I have the acrid taste of rebellion on my lips.
—Anais Nin, *Diary*, Volume One: November 1932[1]

I came out as a teenager, in April 1980: just in time for the election of Ronald Reagan, the AIDS crisis, and the many subsequent marches on Washington for gay and lesbian rights. My personal journal, accompanying me to bars, protest rallies, and poetry readings, became a record of late twentieth-century gay time, paper witness to an arc of change. I'm glad now that I kept my journal close and took notes on those occasions. I had a front-row seat in a cultural movement and took care to describe everything I saw: t-shirt slogans, signs held up at demonstrations, expressions on faces. But my desire to write *everywhere* I went, my belief that what was happening should be remembered, routinely led to backlash from the gay community itself. For in order to create an honest record of growing up and coming out, I was not only writing my own life. I was bringing in and naming the complex lives of others I interacted with (or liked): closeted gay and lesbian friends, closeted teachers. My pen was scarier than a sword for the public school gym teachers I spent the next thirty years chatting with in dinner lines at women's music festivals.

Remember that as late as 2002, before the *Lawrence vs. Texas* decision, being gay was still a criminal identity in many American states—a felony, in fact, when those states selectively applied their archaic sodomy laws (and plenty did). Once outed, you might lose your job, your kids, your housing, your church membership; in Virginia, anyone convicted of a felony lost the right to vote. . . . In short, you were disenfranchised as a citizen and cast out. The cost of disclosure was immeasurable, particularly for teachers and people in the military; undercover operatives did spy on/entrap military servicemen and -women who dared enter gay bars.

To write about the others I observed around me meant some-one might get hurt. At one lesbian rights conference I attended in 1993, a workshop on writing began with the interrogative, "No one here is a journalist, right?" As much as feminism sought to make women's lives and achievements visible, "outing" someone without their permission was understood to be an act of aggression.

Sometimes we cannot write; sometimes we memorize.

❀ ❀ ❀

I was privileged to grow up and come out without fear, due in large part to the infinite support of my unusually hip parents and beloved lesbian cousins. I knew that I liked girls well before I started my first journal; those feelings are evident in stories I wrote and shared by age seven. As a child I came home every day and wrote at the kitchen table, and when (in second grade) I wrote an illustrated love letter to my babysitter Diane, my mother mimeographed it for posterity, thinking it was cute. Little did she know that was just page one of the lifelong romantic oeuvre, before journal-writing drew down a veil of privacy.

My journals contain the full coming-out story, from the first hesitant line at age twelve ["I've been wondering lately if I'm a…"] to the gushing crushes at age thirteen ["I have been REBORN!"] to the first emotional partnership at fourteen ["We held hands all night long, but no one knew. Why is our love looked at with such scorn because we are both women?"]

Like Dorothy's yellow brick road, this was not a fast, linear path to Oz. I also dated boys, and my journals were filled with hesitation and denial; some were literally written in code.[2] But any kid (gay, straight, bi) has a patient listener and tender therapist in a journal, barring its discovery by a vindictive parent, coach, BFF, minister, or burglar. It can be a reliable two-way window, letting light in and reality out.

And what was reality? Aside from the nasty anti-gay graf-fiti one saw everywhere, no realistic images of well-adjusted gay grownups seemed to exist in the mid-1970s. During this same era, the quest for women's legal and economic equality was also jeered by the very mainstream American media charged with reporting on it. Calling the 1970s "the ME decade" reduced feminist and gay rights activism to mere individual selfishness (a view held by hardline Communists as well). Whatever the political bent was in your family home, neither the conservative *New York Daily News* nor the radical *Daily Worker* was about to offer a lonely kid a frank, historical perspective on the gay rights revolution. I suspected that thousands and thousands of other young Americans were writing in their journals, as I did, those half a dozen words: *I think I might be gay.* But who were our pioneers? How had they lived?

As this was light-years before it became possible, convenient, and safe to find accurate resources on the LGBT movement via magazines, the Internet, school support groups, spiritual affinity groups, TV, and film, what we had were library books and pulp novels. Certainly, no teacher in my junior high assigned homework on the Stonewall Riots or the trial of Oscar Wilde. But the journals and diaries of actual gay and lesbian figures could be found right in the literature section of my library. I learned that women once danced together in Depression-era Paris by reading the diary of Anais Nin, whose prolific volumes offered salient points on writing, honesty, and the beauty of women.

Nin's feverish, polyamorous affairs with Henry Miller and his wife, June, were intriguing, but it was her advice on how a writer should deal with homophobic insults in public that gave me a template for activism. In the same entry about being asked to leave a café after dancing intimately with June, Anais Nin writes:

> *. . . I try to explain to her that the writer is the duelist who never fights at the stated hour, who gathers up an insult, like another curious object, a collector's item, spreads it out on his desk later, and then engages in a duel with it verbally. Some people call it weakness. I call it postponement. What is a weakness in the man becomes a quality in the writer. For he preserves, collects what will explode later in his work.*[3]

At eighteen, coming out to my own father, I was grateful as well for Nin's May 1933 entry:

> *And Father comes, resplendent, and we understand each other miraculously. He believes in polarity, man very masculine, woman very feminine. . . . We put brakes on, against our temperament. . . . If my father is going to try to prevent me from breaking loose, then I will hurt him too. He will not tolerate perversity, homosexuality.*[4]

That such writing existed gave me tremendous hope—and, more importantly, context, and a history. Look! Other women kept journals on such things, and rather than being lynched became famous. (However, not ten years later I watched the film *Henry and June* debut in Harvard Square and it was ruined by derisive hoots from Harvard boys appalled by Nin's bisexuality; the lovely scene between Anais and June onscreen met with screams of "Yo, ladies, something's missing," from the party of drunken sophomores seated behind me.)[5]

I made up my mind to be the duelist Nin spoke of: to go beyond mere personal musings in my own journal, to widen the political margins and really list what future generations might want to know. What were we wearing? Singing? Drinking? Watching? How did our garden grow? I committed myself to writing protest letters, letters to editors, letters to Congress. I would "gather up the insult" and challenge homophobia with my fountain pen.

Once I entered college, fresh sources were identified for me by my professors in the emerging field of women's studies. I found the rich literature of women writers and a critical heritage naming conversations between women important. Best of all, there was an entire erudite tradition of journal-keeping women writers all brainily in love with one another: Virginia Woolf and Vita Sackville-West; Gertrude Stein and Alice B. Toklas; Margaret Mead and her tutor, Ruth Benedict; Natalie Barney and practically everyone. I found an almost seamless segue from my own coming out to instant membership in an entire literary tribe.

❊ ❊ ❊

In practice, however, I quickly learned that my own real partners detested the idea that I might be writing about them in that God-damned journal; worse, I seemed to require a lot of time alone, away from them, in order to write; and worst of all, I considered writing about them to be some sort of compliment, not a deplorable habit that should be eliminated. One lover shouted that I was only interested in women so I could write about them; another snarled, "I can't tell you how many times I've awakened to find you writing in your journal," to which I replied, "If you don't make me want to write, I have no business waking up next to you in the first place." And my Brazilian lover objected that it wasn't so much my journal, but the fact that I wrote about her *in English* (the oppressor's language of the colonizing America).

One girlfriend brazenly read my journal, desperate to find out if I rated her the best lover I'd ever had; caught red-handed, she merely criticized my choice of adjectives for her techniques. Another one kept phoning to ask, "So you'll come over when you're done writing? When will you be done writing? Will you ever be done?" And one woman remarked on my many journals, yet encouraged my writing life by giving me expensive pens, including one that wrote in the dark.

Writing about love and sex is a kind of naming and claiming, a grammatical conjugation of relationships: *I think I might love her. Oh, how I love her. I loved her so. I love her still.* Journal-keeping (and the draining publication of memoir) allows the jilted lover, the one left, to have the final word, the parting shot of wanting. And the journal continues as a one-sided conversation with one's flame — as Colette wrote in *Claudine Married:*

> *This will no longer really be Claudine's diary any more, because in it I can talk of nothing but Rezi. What has happened to the old, quick-witted Claudine? She is nothing but a fevered, unhappy creature drifting weakly in Rezi's wake.*[6]

I learned that my journal was perceived as threatening because, while I didn't always get the girl, I kept the conversations. I had, on paper, landmarks and islands of discrete beloved moments, incidents a love tourist might visit, looking back. Journals capture personal erotic memoir with which no pornography can compare, and to re-read one's account of a genuine love is to re-experience all the heat, commitment, and sublime everyday detail. As the gay male community around me began to be devastated by AIDS through the 1980s, vibrant personalities whose lives ended early remained forever young, alive, and remembered in the journals of their surviving partners — although to reopen such pages was heart-wrenching, not an hour's casual stroll through the past.

A more difficult issue for gay and lesbian writers, throughout history, is legal entrapment through a diary or "little black book." (*The Scarlet Professor,* about Smith College literary critic Newton Arvin, describes the seizure of Arvin's diary by homophobic state police in 1960.)[7] I experienced the gay community's fear of notebooks first-hand, because for many years I took my journal with me into women's bars.

Writing in Bars

By the time I was of legal drinking age (18 or 19, back in 1980) and could enter women's bars, desire and inspiration mingled on my fountain pen. But in the heavily separatist, plaid-flannel era of early '80s lesbian culture I was already suspect, in part due to my wholesome, "straight," girl-next-door appearance. A community paranoid (for good reasons) about being infiltrated by FBI operatives greeted my interest in writing with the abrupt, "Look, sister, are you even gay?" Was I a spy? A narc? An informant? Worst of all—an anthropologist? For there were class issues, too, being heatedly debated in women's communities, and this further complicated my identity as a graduate student. I was hanging out with working-class women, many of whom were hostile to being "studied." Although women's studies programs and feminist writers were on the front lines of the LGBT movement, pushing for the inclusion of more lesbian voices in academia, many times my drinking companions jeered me with "Ph.D., huh? Means *piled higher and deeper.*"

Well-meaning women took me aside and explained that one didn't come down to the bar to write. But I did. I didn't really enjoy drinking, and I was a disaster at the pool table. I wanted to do what I liked best—writing in my journal—in lesbian space. Wasn't it my space, too? Wasn't this all about freedom of choice? Apparently not. Still, "What are you writing there, hon?" is as good an urban icebreaker as any other line.

Despite the challenges, for many years I kept a bar journal. Smaller than my regular 8x11-inch notebook, it slid into the pocket of my black leather jacket when I headed out to drag-king nights and poetry slams at clubs. I filled it up with club cards and flyers, notes on friends' performances, dates of upcoming rallies, and, naturally, some phone numbers as well. The brief lines of description, though, and little bits of dialogue—that's the part I'm glad I dared to write.

On bar nights we all glow in the dark. The recessed blacklights here turn t-shirt and journal pages blinding white, my flesh and leather jacket plum black.

A half-moon shaped counter with a lot of knee-to-knee history beneath it; another city landmark of first meetings unseen by the aerial news helicopter.

A woman crying into feeble bar napkins — who dumped her? — says, "This life can be a hardship post." A very young woman in a faded field hockey sweatshirt lights a cigarette and throws down the shaken match, so cute it hurts the skin. I walk home, past the house where Langston Hughes once lived.

Pasta, being delivered for the birthday party, steams up the windows; overheard: "What's your type?" "Oh, neurotic genius."

Tonight everything good that can happen does, the recipe of environment that very seldom happens: not too much smoke, not too much crowd, just enough space to move around and mingle, a show onstage that makes all of us laugh in unison.

Overheard: "Where was I when my shirt burst open?"

There is a look that passes between two women that says, It could have happened but it ain't gonna. I could have had you but let's just not ever mention it, shall we? It's an eye-blink of a relationship, a sizing-up and letting-go in one inchoate breath.

A female cabaret performer named Gina Tonic shouts from the stage, "My hair is just short enough to let the butch on the street know why I'm looking at her."

A big tough woman with her neck to one side checks it all out, blows smoke sideways out one lip corner, hand around a bottleneck, haircut freshly buzzed; more pockets than lockets on her.

Halloween party. I admire a woman's police uniform and tell her she looks hot. My bad: turns out she's an actual policewoman, on duty here tonight. Oops.

There's a young drag king onstage who owes me a five-page paper.

Another bar patron has her notebook out. I ask her what SHE'S writing, and she's on to me: "You're Dr. Morris, aren't you?" And I'm alive forever, and all of it is true.

As this illustrates, by the 1990s I had other comrades in writing at bars. J. Sapinoso and the late Cheryl Spector were beloved, esteemed, spiritually dedicated observers and documentary activists who, like me, operated within a code of ethics and were accepted. This change in attitude toward the "recording" of a subculture was caused by three interesting trends: first, the availability and use of social networking tools like cell phones with cameras and text-messaging applications, so that mini-videos and birthday snapshots were now taken in bars and posted online without every patron's permission. Second, do-it-yourself music production and the hustle to become a known "brand" in a depressed economy meant that almost everyone was packaging and self-promoting their work as an artist of some kind (recording, graphic design, poetry, tattoo work). But most exciting as far as I was concerned was the resurgence of poetry and spoken word into a hybrid bar/coffeehouse culture for writers. Spoken-word slams began to compete with club nights for tribes of restless, intelligent young women.

Mothertongue

By 1998, D.C. had a women's spoken-word stage, Mothertongue, founded by a trio of smart lesbian activists as a supportive space for women of all sexual and gender orientations. Each month, hundreds of women packed the Black Cat to read their work aloud onstage—invariably, slams *read from their journals*. When I first stumbled into the Black Cat on D.C.'s hip and gritty 14th Street one frozen February night to discover numberless young poets with pierced navels bellying up to the mic to scream about street harassment, I thought I'd died and gone to heaven, though I was already twice the age of most women in the room. It was that very age difference that made an impact: when I sat down that night, Noabeth stood up and flexed her arms and took up space like twice the wimp I'd been at twenty-two. There followed two dozen women each as compelling as the one before her, and everyone was writing in their journals *at the bar*, and their prose and poems shouted YES: I am the woman, black, Jewish, Latina, South Asian Muslim, indigenous/invisible/unseen; I am the foot on racism's neck; I am the one they raped who lived; I am the young queer scene writ large. It was an open-mic garden of Eden, and Adam discreetly mixed the drinks. Eve was in every line of spoken word, and all the fruit was luscious, ripe, split open by language, and girls were swapping pens.

And everyone knew everyone. So, how long had this been going on? Where did they all come from? All these hip and curvy, scruffy, buffy girls with notebooks, tender pages clutched in sweaty palms, silver rings on fingers, nose rings, ARMS. Red henna hair tossed back, throats cleared, GO: you have five minutes or three poems. So this was passion, written out by hand, memorized, delivered, slammed, applauded.

Mothertongue appeared at a specific moment. Women's bookstores were closing; they had long served as presentation spaces for radical feminist writers whose work went unheard in mainstream venues. Male spoken word was taking off, flying on wings of urban rap and the need to empower, through literacy, young black men in prison; but too often public poetry slams were male-dominated, both in participation and through spoken lines dissing women; thus Mothertongue was born (and continues twelve years on). It came each month like any woman's menses: third Wednesday night, doors opening after 8, $5 sliding scale, and a line of creased black jackets down the block. Low lighting and dark walls, drumming followed by announcements, round tables, whistling crowds. "It's the only scene in town," I emailed all my loved ones. "Fresh, fresh, fresh wordplay, delivered homestyle." Spreading the word ("Word to the Mothertongue!") brought mixed results from my middle-aging pals; I brought one old friend whose nervous comment was "young crowd," meaning, *not for us*. She fled. But you had to be a writer, see. I had an ageless hunger fed each month.

Month after month, I never heard anyone bomb, though half the readers hung their heads in shyness. The nervewrack of Mothertongue, once I started getting up onstage and slamming my own work old-school, was seeing a line of my own college students dash into the front row just as I launched into a fairly erotic piece. Fine; so they knew their professor had a local lie; but still, seeing the same faces in class the next day could bring a blush to my blazered throat. Turn in your midterms, please, and oh, yes, how did you like that poem I read last night?

Poetry spilled over into other bars, as writing became as much a part of open-mic nights as guitar acts. One night at Phase One, the oldest continually operating women's bar in Washington, D.C., open-mic night ended with an actual public writing game. The emcee handed out slips of paper to every table and commanded every woman present to join in: one sentence from each table, a collective poem comparing beautiful women to delicious vegetables. A frenzy of writing ensued, and I watched with astonishment—at the bar were several of my own students who normally rejected/procrastinated any kind of poetry assignment. But this was an exercise in group identity, in a public but safe place: *our place*. And the emcee created spontaneous erotica from our irreverent one-liners.

Places of Rage

Though the gay and lesbian community has produced more than its share of brilliant writers, this hasn't necessarily added up to social approval or admiration, as the history of censorship reflects. In fact, in notoriously anti-intellectual American culture, being a bookworm or writing in your journal at lunchtime used to be proof you were at least a little bit queer, for both boys and girls: look at how both male and female librarians are stereotyped as *unmarried* or sexually marginal in some way. But librarians are great cataloguers. And, too often, the function of writing in the gay community has been to catalogue the outrages against us. In the fabulous words of poet Allan Gurganus, "Anger is a kind of B-emotion. *Rage* is as clear as gin."[8]

I kept a bar journal to capture moments of ordinary and extraordinary intimacy, neighborhood noise and celebration. The bar journal crossed borders of public and private space. But my regular journal continued to be the duelist, as Nin's ghost had instructed.

Right after Matthew Shepard was killed, I joined other Washingtonians for the spontaneous rally on Capitol Hill—where Ellen DeGeneres read a hastily scrawled speech right from her ripped-out journal page. All around me I saw others, too, writing speeches and protest letters *by hand*; yes, we write after heartbreak, after shock, after events that crack us open. The words pour out. And a celebrity like Ellen does a public service by affirming the uses of journal-writing to heal (instead of turning to drink, drugs, vengeance). On that night in 1998, as I crouched on a wall at the

Capitol, I was transcribing the words from Ellen's journal right into my own, the direct pipeline of writing in public places. Whatever happened to gay people, we had to archive for ourselves; not even my beloved *Washington Post* was going to report our point of view. On that night, I noted, one politician intoned, "Now is not the time for anger," but the crowd roared "Yes, it is."

The morning after that rally at the Capitol I was at the National Zoo, writing in my journal, when I noticed a very effeminate twelve-year-old boy watching me closely. I recognized him as the sort of kid other kids would identify and torment as "so gay." And he recognized me.

"What are you writing?" he asked me.

"I'm describing the people I saw at a rally last night, and the very moving words they had to say."

"Are you a psychologist?" he wanted to know. This suggested, to me, that he'd already been to one. Perhaps concerned grownups were already writing notes on him.

We chatted about writing. He said he wrote stories, but no journal yet—"I'm only twelve." Between us, on the bench, was a newspaper with Matthew Shepard's photo in the fold: this was what awaited him, the threat of martyrdom, crucifixion. How could I urge him to seize shelter, or power, through his writing? Should I come out to him, tell him *I know what you're going through*, when perhaps his self-awareness was still dormant? Should I assure him it was possible to grow up gay and proud? I carefully navigated these waters as we talked, beginning with "I started my journal at twelve." He listened to every word. When we parted, we shook hands gravely, like lawyers. I said, "It was an honor to make your acquaintance." Five years of high school lay ahead for him to find his voice, the crucible forging a writer of the next generation. And would a journal be enough to pull him through?

---

[1] Anais Nin, *The Diary of Anais Nin: Volume One, 1931-1934.* New York: Swallow Press and Harcourt, Brace & World, Inc., 1966; p. 144.

[2] This was also true for Alison Bechdel, who revisits her adolescent journal coding in the graphic novel *Fun Home.* Mariner, 2007; pp. 140-143, 169-172.

[3] Anais Nin, ibid., p. 145.

[4] Ibid., p. 214.

[5] Not that Nin's diaries must be approached only as a sacred subject. A really amusing jab at her famous writings was popularized by lesbian stand-up comic Marga Gomez, whose skit "The Lost Disneyland Diaries of Anais Nin"—featuring a fervid encounter between Nin and Minnie Mouse—convulsed audiences at women's music festivals throughout the 1990s.

[6] Colette, *Claudine Married*. Ballantine, 1983 (Farrar, Straus & Giroux), p. 113.

[7] See Andrew Holleran, "Arrested For Sex," in *Out* magazine, May 2001, p. 73.

[8] Remark from a speech at the OutWrite Conference, March 1992.

Devon Browning, *The Kitchen*, oil on linen, 15" x 20"

Ars Poetica: [We'll Take Our Turn, Singing/ Dirty Rap Songs]

The world needs more drag
you out into the street poetry—
enough with the dishwashing
watching your kid throw a fuck
-ing baseball for the first time.
Give me all that you can't pick up
the phone and tell someone.
No more *souls*
or *truth* or *freedom*—abort
your breathy abstractions.
All my (wo)men moderately pissed off,
come to the page ink-tongue spitting.
The best of all the dirty words is:
complacency—next to: normative—next to:
meta. And for the writer who's breathing
without seething over love's legality
or the sensitivity of someone else's womb—
I've got something for his punkass:
trigger after trigger of untouchable topics,
a love for the words *pussy* and *chartreuse*,
a whole catalog of men ass shaking lines.
Boy, where you came from
is not where you are. E. Bishop,
the baddest of all bitches, said, *write it!*,
Yoshimi, it'd be tragic if those evil robots
win. If we settled for so much mediocre meditation
(the fluff, fluff, pass of cute poems),
I'd order a recession
on all your bullshit.
Some books should be burned.
Can you hear the gear flick of my Bic
hungry for all those darlings you've wasted?

Release Your Fear: The War Cries of Hummingbirds

Your car radio is the kind of broken
in which it'll play only ELO
because it's a stuck cassette
and the tips need to go towards heat.
The breakup happens near the freeway
in between the left-turn signal's beep.
The magic is the fucking song finally changing,
the moment of surreal explosion, a Ferris wheel in reverse.
I just want you in my head,
my little, dirty mongrel mind,
listening until the loop takes over
its own mad orchestra.

❀

You wanted the end to have been fireworks in February,
you wanted it to be all water-color run-off.
The tornado named Samantha comes into the bar and kisses you,
slams her purse of broken men beside me.
She drinks all the freebies and bats her eyes at you at me.
The blue Earth turns black when she says *so, who are you again?*
And you fill her up, pour us a round, and try to give me some light.
When you two walk out, you leave me
my hips: a hungry tidal wave.
This is another wreck: another reason to let birds play
with my hair again.

❀

You drink until
the face behind you is your favorite dead blond boy.
You count their money like communion,
genuflect like the rug's quicksand.
Name your next broken-hearted storm after me.
Count the floating men
as I close their eyes,
take my lips to their neck-nape
and say *try again, try again you goddamn little fool.*

Postcard: Your Wife in 30 Years

How she managed the barbed courtyard
fence in torrential rain is heroic.

And she's holding your painting, inscribed *Giovanni's
Room,* and Edna St. Vincent Millay's poetry
and I'm unable to understand a word because

I speak only Dutch now and roll American cigarettes
and live on a canal in The Netherlands with my Italian-
Polish-Hungarian-Czechoslovakian lover, who by then

is famous and you are too, by somehow finding a cave
in every little line I've scrawled since you left your shirt
and, naked, waved your arms like the lone madman,

and she's saying to me: *Who were you to him?* And I try
to tell her, *I'm sorry, I'm writing. Please come back later,*
and her smudged lips keep flipping and the rain

keeps on keepin' on and we're both inconsolable wrecks.
And she's got this book in her hands,
in all its black-threaded attempted atonement,

and it still reeks of the switchblade rust and in our most intimate
moment, in which her visit is justified, she says your name
in all its beauty. For the first time it floats
around the room, and stone

muscles move just to find forgotten syllables
and the word for *Wildfeuer,*
and she says death and the reddest part

of her lip quivers. As she speaks,
I can only hear the ice-cream truck weaseling
in the distance, I'm aware

of all the gull cries,
the deepest of canals,
and all our unconquerable space.

The Poem in Which the Apocalypse Doesn't Go So Terribly

We're in a town ten miles from Tuscaloosa.
We've imported hanging moss because you're sick
of my stories about men
just swingin' like that.

Today the news is all good:
because we haven't talked to anyone
and the booze we make in the backyard
is full of only airglow and moonmilk.

Before we moved here, things just fell down:
first a satellite and then, one by one,
planes, birds, and when our house was hit
with a blimp, we felt lucky.

In this town of just the two of us,
I don't question your choke-grip,
you do not hold my wrist for daily inspection.
At night, we fuck the trailer park out of each other.

The men who used to live and burn
things in our mosquito alley would've responded.
As if we were the last coyotes,
as if you could forget why and how a thing howls.

Duet

Your snap strict, instructive
as a metronome, you'd stand
aside, reminding me of my
mediocrity. Now I know why
you insisted I learn to live
within the song, bars & notes
like rows of trees in winter & us
two plastic figures epoxied
out of random parts and fixed
inside a globe, perpetually
walking the path lined with lindens
behind the shotgun we lived
in then. Shaken, the scene blurs,
branches closing behind us.
When the whiteout subsided,
the carriage clock you loved
to say you'd gotten for a song
stopped. So time was
an abundance or absence
of tires sighing through slush
& at intervals, to be sure I was
still breathing, a train
came to shake the dust that settled
over everything we owned.
At night, at least, I could still speak
our dying tongue to a spirit
between fits of sleep,
fractious minutes, passing
headlights sweeping patterns
over the wall. I couldn't bring myself
to touch the pianos, but couldn't stop
snapping shots of branches,
zooming until they revealed
their tangle of nerves,
needles of light defining the spaces
in between, as if an image

repeated assumes meaning.
The thing I love most
about falling snow? The way
it transcribes silence.
Words. Songs. The puzzle
we started (of course,
a winter scene) stayed undone.
That was the year with only
a frame & bit of blue sky

Ashley Inguanta, photograph

Sudden as Spring

While I slept in your grandmother's dank bedroom
and you juiced oranges in the kitchen, you needed me—
and not like before, not a half-lust born of proximity—
you craved me newly, and I belonged to someone else.
And while he wrote lesson plans in state in the desert,

you drove your blue sedan into a neighborhood like apparition:
one with a craggy shore we strode carefully, and in the
coy tide of early evening we found a message in a bottle.
The message was mundane for such cosmic delivery,
still we considered ourselves charmed.

When we pitched our reply from a ferry, a man
with a knife in his belt watched us, limped close.
But by land, we forgot him
footsteps synchronized.

The day before I left, you came out to your family—told me
I made you brave. Let me let it alone now.

You loved me for a time
then like all things sudden and warm,
there was an end to my muse-hood.

When I left to meet
my man in a shadowed forest,
a cold and quiet rain
swept the earth away under our tent,
and with it, me

with my solitary, unseen scar
between my breasts:
your name.

Tomorrow

This face you find in the mirror
alters again, imperceptibly.
Trust me: the eyes stay the same.

Rooms become a road
trod morning to evening, the path to the kitchen,
your fingers trailing a banister,
that bed another milestone
welcome as a dent in the pillow.

Dear warrior, you can withstand the years,
even waltz with them.
Run through the garden at night
when the moon fills its bowl of milk again
and your path is crossed by snails.

Sweet in the Air

with a line by Scott Miles

I'm searching for the gorgeous man who sang

"Foolish Games" in Indianapolis

I never know what to do with my arms

What is the genre of the motion

How hot is the steam in the steam room

I have never been to Fire Island

Tonight I want a shawl of fox fur

Secondhand

Tell me how long the train ride

Tell me the story of the French duchess

Nothing to do but lie around like a famous painting on the ceiling

Tell me I can look until I die

There had better be frescoes in hell

At least a cute café I can take Dürer to

Tell me how long to look at myself

I don't know how to ask for youth

I don't know what color to paint my nails

The manicurist is tall and strong

I want to invite him to the kiki

I want to wrap him in blue toile

It isn't cold enough yet for tea

But how can I ignore this orange antique set

The sugar bowl alone is worth the price

Everything rattles in transit

I will learn whatever language I need to

How fast can we run without letting go our hands

See how our scarves unwind in the wind

See the photographer

See centuries later the oil painting

See survival

Papery light for days

Gin on the chaise with a patient man

The Glow of Your Former Self

I keep a smoky quartz crystal on my desk

How to remember your mother

How to feel about moving half a country away

Dot dot dot look another cornfield

People aren't always joking when you think they are

Wasps are known to refuse breaking from their parade

Which isn't to say you should run through it

It's always someone's job to clean up the mess

Let us personify time so he can feel included

Let us personify the galaxy so she can feel her power

What are the tasks we have been given

Blood blood candle wax stingers and blood

She feels gravity more when she's barefoot

She feels gravity more in skyscrapers

She would prefer not to

Let us think about time as we do in novels

Talk about everything in the present tense

The wolf is in grandmother's bed

The wolf is a metaphor for the sun

Why would you try to escape from the heliopause

I have a tattoo of the spacecraft Voyager 1

The tattoo is a metaphor for communication

What I know about communication is you must love

The candles are lit but they're not the point

Moonlight is sunlight reflected

The sparkle in her eyes is sunlight reflected

The sun is a metaphor for time

Every last star is dead or dying

You could spend your life to get there for nothing

Best to take with you a green memory

Best to take with you a flare

Voyager One *Imagines Becoming Andromeda*

Like Pythia, Apollo will seize my voice,
quake meaning from my tracking device
& make monsters clip coupons
to purchase distance.
Like Tiresias, I will drift on borders,
mistaking sex for love,
a mirror for the curve of space.
When I've seen too much
I'll trade my eyes
for the ecstasy of being right.

A Sibyl at Theta Serpentis,
I'll cross the sky in slow boredom,
waiting for petitioners
that never make the pilgrimage
from earth to my hollow.
At Dadona, they'll see me pass
and know to mark the holy days,
candles lit to mimic
hydrogen's stellar burn.
Cassandra at Casseopeia,
snakes will comb my hair
and suck my ears
until the bell of space rings
in my bird-boned throat.
With no one to hear me sing
I will not believe my own disaster.

Void of Course

Voyager Two
0.0 degrees in Cancer
April 5-12, 1978

Shush me up and leave me on the mountain.
I'm slim with potential out here.
Drive me to silence like the moon turns void,
her face hung on a hook at the zodiac's end.

She shrugs from symbol to bloom: a sign
without metaphor, a heave without ghost.
Dew-eyed astrologers quiet their star charts,
fat hens in the garden keep eggs to themselves.

Around me the sky will forget its message,
cease sending static to command my turn.
Let the scientists rot, worrying my failure.
I didn't ask to carry the future in my stomach,

to burst it out for god knows what to find.
I'm a broken monster / girl / thing.
My mouth is made of tremble / radio / suck.
There isn't language out here to make me shine.

Pointed Towards Supernova 1987A, Voyager Two *Considers the Relativity of Beauty*

Slip of shock wave /
of lace thinned against stretched thighs /
of silicone /
of being the right girl at the right time —

The sky spits and gasps —
an echo of touch /
a veil of dust /
hems unthreading from urgency.

Whirl up pink light,
pearl-strung light,
up in to the stellar wind.
Luminosity is a function of time.

If this is what dying looks like,
then let me die.
Let me be fire
wrung from good black stone.

The Voyagers in Couples' Therapy, as Imagined by Voyager Two

She says   comfort is not the immediate goal,
             spun from a world we can't claim as our own.

She says   we need to begin our statements with *I*,
             glean ourselves from the universe's brash becoming.

She says   grief—like farming, like art—is a folded map,
             its utility pointless as candlelight or butter churns.

             Love, we are beyond it, aren't we? Breathless,
             full of data colonies and hardware.
             What lives in us isn't the fragment and thrust
             of modernism or the swing-swung sway of blues
             unfurling from a trumpet's petal'd bell.
             What lives in us, oh, O, I don't know—
             I've grown sour from trying to explain myself
             to well-intentioned stars in their good shoes,
             to planets spun drunk with gravity.

             I want a couch.

             A cup of tea.

             White noise pouring from a well-placed fan.

             I want tissues.

             The soft kind.

             Pulled from a sky-blue box with kittens
             tumbling on the side.

             I want you there to pluck me from my endlessness,
             applauding my *I* sprung from *us*,
             satellited in the lush rush of description.

Liz Ahl is the author of the chapbooks *Talking About The Weather* (Seven Kitchens, 2012), *Luck* (Pecan Grove Press, 2010), and *A Thirst That's Partly Mine*, which won the 2008 Slapering Hol Press chapbook competition. Her work has appeared recently in *Panoply, Pittsburgh Poetry Review,* and *Ecotone*. She lives in Holderness, New Hampshire.

Nico Amador is a writer, educator, and community organizer in Philadelphia, Pennsylvania. His work has been published in *MiPOesias, APIARY Magazine, Poet Lore, Plenitude Magazine,* and the Big Blue Marble Bookstore, and has been accepted to the forthcoming book *Joto: An Anthology of Queer Chicano/a Poetry*. Amador contributes as co-editor of Thread Makes Blanket Press and is a member of the Rogue River Writing Workshop.

Derrick Austin is the author of *Trouble the Water* (BOA Editions, Spring 2016), selected by Mary Szybist for the 2015 A. Poulin Jr. Prize. A Cave Canem fellow, he earned his M.F.A. from the University of Michigan. His work has appeared in *The Best American Poetry 2015, Image, New England Review, Callaloo, Crab Orchard Review, The Paris-American, Memorious,* and other journals and anthologies. He is the social media coordinator for *The Offing Magazine*.

Heather Bartlett holds an M.F.A. in poetry from Hunter College. Her work can be found in *Barrow Street, Connotation Press, The Nervous Breakdown, Ninth Letter, Phoebe, PMS poemmemoirstory,* and other journals. She is a lecturer in English at the State University of New York at Cortland. She lives and writes in Ithaca, New York.

Ellen Bass's poetry collections include *Like a Beggar, The Human Line,* and *Mules of Love*, and she co-edited an anthology of women's poetry, *No More Masks!*. Her work has been frequently published in *The New Yorker, The American Poetry Review,* and other journals. She is co-author of several nonfiction books, including *The Courage to Heal*. She teaches in the M.F.A. program at Pacific University in Forest Grove, Oregon.

Jeffery Beam's works include *New Beautiful Tendons: Collected Queer Poems 1969–2012, Visions of Dame Kind, Broken Flower, Gospel Earth,* and *What We Have Lost* (CD). His *Life of the Bee* premiered as a song cycle by Lee Hoiby at Carnegie Hall. Steven Serpa used Beam's poem to compose *Heaven's Birds*, which premiered during Boston's World AIDS Day. Beam lives in Hillsborough, North Carolina, with his husband.

Jessica Rae Bergamino is the author of several chapbooks, most recently *The Desiring Object* (Sundress Publications). Individual poems may be found or are forthcoming in *Gulf Coast, Slice, West Branch, Southern*

Humanities Review, The Journal, and other journals. She is a Ph.D. student at the University of Utah, where she is a poetry editor for *Quarterly West.*

CHARLIE BONDHUS's second poetry book, *All the Heat We Could Carry,* won the 2014 Thom Gunn Award for Gay Poetry. His work appears in journals including *Poetry Magazine, Bellevue Literary Review,* and *The Missouri Review.* He is assistant professor of English at Raritan Valley Community College (New Jersey) and is poetry editor at *The Good Men Project.*

DEAN ANTHONY BRINK's poetry has appeared in *Columbia Poetry Review, Exquisite Corpse: A Journal of Letters and Life, Going Down Swinging, Cordite Poetry Review, New Writing, The Portland Review, Taiwan kadan,* and the anthology *In Protest.* He also translates poetry from Chinese and Japanese and composes for piano. He is an associate professor in the Department of Foreign Languages and Literatures, National Chiao Tung University, Taiwan.

RACHEL BROWNSON is a writer and hospital chaplain in Ann Arbor, Michigan. She received her M.F.A. in poetry from Warren Wilson College, and her work appears or is forthcoming in *Four Way Review, The Collagist, The Toast, The Christian Century,* and other journals. She is a member of Rabble Collective.

KRISTI CARTER is a Ph.D. student in Poetry, specializing in Women's and Gender Studies, at University of Nebraska-Lincoln. Her poems have appeared in publications such as *So to Speak, PMS poemmemoirstory, CALYX,* and *Hawai'i Review.* Her work examines the intersection of gender and intergenerational trauma in 20th-century poetics. She holds an M.F.A. from Oklahoma State University and is at work on a collection of poems.

MORGAN CARTER is a senior at West Virginia Wesleyan College, where they will graduate with a double major in Creative Writing and Gender Studies. They hope to continue their studies as a graduate student in the fall. They currently reside in West Virginia, where they are an active member in the queer community and its local activism.

DOUG PAUL CASE lives in Bloomington, Indiana, where he works in Indiana University's art history department and edits *Word Riot.* He is the author of the chapbooks *Something to Hide My Face In* (Seven Kitchens, 2015) and *College Town* (Porkbelly Press, 2015).

CASSIA CHAMBERS-GAMMILL, while living in Portland, Oregon, for the last ten years, has enjoyed playing in bands and volunteering for youth organizations such as Rock and Roll Camp for Girls and Queer Rock Camp. She's a working-class, queer single parent and gives a shout-out and thank-you to parent allies everywhere.

JAMES CIHLAR is the author of two poetry books, *Rancho Nostalgia* and *Undoing*, and the chapbooks *A Conversation with My Imaginary Daughter* and *Metaphysical Bailout*. His writing has appeared in *The American Poetry Review*, *The Threepenny Review*, and *Lambda Literary*.

JACKIE CRAVEN has published in journals such as *Chautauqua*, *Mid-American Review*, *New Ohio Review*, *Salamander*, and *Water~Stone Review*. Her poem "Southbound" appeared in the fall 2014 issue of *Nimrod International Journal*. A chapbook of flash fiction, *Our Lives Became Unmanageable*, is forthcoming from Omnidawn. She completed her Doctor of Arts in writing at the University at Albany-SUNY.

KIMBERLY DARK is a writer, mother, performer, and professor. She is the author of five award-winning solo performance scripts, and her poetry and prose appear in several publications. She tours widely in the English-speaking world. Her shows have been named in *Curve Magazine*'s top-ten performances of the year, and Campus Pride named her as one of 25 "Best of the Best" speakers and performers on college campuses in 2010.

NICHOLAS DeBELLIS, winner of the Lon Otto Prize in Prose, studied creative writing and physics at the University of St. Thomas in St. Paul, Minnesota.

LISA DORDAL, M.Div., M.F.A., author of *Commemoration*, from Finishing Line Press, teaches in the English Department at Vanderbilt University. Her poetry has appeared in a variety of journals, including *Best New Poets*, *CALYX*, *Cave Wall*, *The Greensboro Review*, *Sojourners*, *New Millennium Writings*, and *Journal of Feminist Studies in Religion*.

JULIE R. ENSZER, Ph.D., is the author of three poetry collections, *Lilith's Demons* (A Midsummer Night's Press, 2015), *Sisterhood* (Sibling Rivalry Press, 2013), and *Handmade Love* (A Midsummer Night's Press, 2010). She is editor of *Milk and Honey: A Celebration of Jewish Lesbian Poetry* (A Midsummer Night's Press, 2011), which was a finalist for the Lambda Literary Award in Lesbian Poetry.

SHELLEY ETTINGER's first novel, *Vera's Will*, was published in 2015. Her current novel-in-progress is suggested by the life, death, and afterlife of Kitty Genovese. Her work has been published in *Nimrod International Journal*, *Mississippi Review*, *Cream City Review*, *Stone Canoe*, *Mizna*, and other journals. A longtime LGBTQ activist, she lives in New York City and works as a university secretary.

NICOLE FIX is a recipient of the Elizabeth George Foundation Grant and was a finalist for *Glimmer Train*'s Very Short Fiction Award and *Nimrod*'s Katherine Anne Porter Prize. Her fiction has appeared in journals including *Post Road Magazine*. She holds a B.F.A. from New York University's Tisch School of the Arts and an M.F.A. from the Yale School of Drama.

MARY GILLILAND, author of the forthcoming poetry memoir *We Are All Immortals*, has taught writing at Cornell University and Namgyal Monastery Institute of Buddhist Studies. She has been a Stanley Kunitz Fellow and a featured poet at the International Al Jazeera Film Festival. Her poetry has appeared in *AGNI*, *Hotel Amerika*, *Notre Dame Review*, *Poetry*, and *The &Now Awards: The Best Innovative Writing*.

SARAH GIRAGOSIAN's poems have appeared or are forthcoming in such journals as *Crazyhorse*, *Prairie Schooner*, *The Missouri Review*, *Blackbird*, and *Verse Daily*, among others. A winner of the *American Poetry Journal* Book Prize, her first book, *Queer Fish*, is under contract with *Dream Horse Press* and will be published in 2016. She teaches in the Department of Writing and Critical Inquiry at the University at Albany-SUNY.

BENJAMIN S. GROSSBERG is Director of Creative Writing at the University of Hartford. His books include *Space Traveler* (University of Tampa, 2014) and *Sweet Core Orchard* (University of Tampa, 2009), winner of the 2008 *Tampa Review* Prize and a Lambda Literary Award.

ROBERT HAMBERGER has been awarded a Hawthornden Fellowship and was shortlisted for a Forward prize. He won first prize in *Chroma*'s International Queer Writing Competition, 2006, and has appeared in anthologies internationally. His collections are *Warpaint Angel* (1997), *The Smug Bridegroom* (2002), and *Torso* (2007). His collection *Blue Wallpaper* is forthcoming from Waterloo Press. He lives in Brighton, England.

COURTNEY HARTNETT earned an M.F.A. in poetry at the University of North Carolina at Greensboro, where she currently teaches in the English department. Her poems and prose have appeared or are forthcoming in *Appalachian Journal*, *Gertrude Press*, *storySouth*, *Bombay Gin Literary Journal*, and other journals. She was a finalist for the *Crab Orchard Review*'s 2014 Allison Joseph Poetry Award.

FRANCINE KAYE HENDRICKSON is from Asheville, North Carolina. She received her B.A. in Creative Writing from SUNY Purchase College. She is a recent recipient of the Gilman Scholarship, which allowed her to study in India, as well as the Ginny Wray Senior Prize in Poetry. Her work has been featured on platforms such as The Apollo Theater, Barclays Center, and the Gotham Series of Young Writers.

THEODOSIA HENNEY juggles, bakes, and sews bowties. Her work has appeared in publications including *Rattle*, *dirtcakes*, and *Triggerfish Critical Review*, and she has appeared as a fellow at the 2014 Lambda Literary Emerging Writers retreat and the Orion Environmental Writers Conference at Breadloaf. She is the Poetry Editor at *Cactus Heart Press* and entertains ambitions of someday owning a blazer in every color.

KATE LYNN HIBBARD's books of poems are *Sleeping Upside Down*, *Sweet Weight*, and *When We Become Weavers: Queer Female Poets on the Midwest Experience* (editor), and she is working on a manuscript of historical poetry about women's experiences in the Great Plains frontier. She teaches creative writing, composition, and women's studies at Minneapolis Community and Technical College.

MATTHEW HITTINGER is the author of *The Erotic Postulate* (2014) and *Skin Shift* (2012), both from Sibling Rivalry Press. He received his M.F.A. from the University of Michigan, where he won a Hopwood Award. In 2012, *Poets & Writers Magazine* named him a Debut Poet on their eighth annual list. He lives and works in New York City.

KAI HOFIUS is a queer and non-binary trans software engineer living, working, and writing in the Bay Area. Their poetry has appeared in *Conceptions Southwest* and *Open Ear of the Universe*.

LEAH HORLICK is a writer from Saskatoon currently living on Unceded Coast Salish Territories in Vancouver. She is the author of two books of poetry, *Riot Lung* (Thistledown Press, 2012) and *For Your Own Good* (Caitlin Press, 2015). She co-curates *Reverb Magazine*, Vancouver's only queer and anti-oppressive reading series, with her dear friend Esther McPhee.

ANNIE ITA is a 17-year-old high school senior in Amherst, Massachusetts. She is bisexual and a member of her school's Gender and Sexuality Alliance. She will attend art school in the fall to pursue a B.F.A. in Ceramics.

WAYNE JOHNS's poems have appeared in *New England Review*, *Ploughshares*, *Prairie Schooner*, *Image*, and other journals. His work has been anthologized in *Best New Poets 2014*, *Don't Leave Hungry: 50 Years of Southern Poetry Review*, and *Gaslight: Lambda Literary Emerging Voices*.

LAURA JOK received her M.F.A. at the University of Houston, where she served as fiction editor for *Gulf Coast: A Journal of Literature and Fine Arts*. Her story "As It Were" won third place in *Glimmer Train*'s August 2014 Short Story Award for New Writers. Her fiction also has appeared in *Alaska Quarterly Review*. She lives in Evanston, Illinois.

ALYSE KNORR is author of *Copper Mother* (Switchback Books) and *Annotated Glass* (Furniture Press Books), as well as the chapbooks *Epithalamia* (Horse Less Press) and *Alternates* (dancing girl press). She received her M.F.A. from George Mason University. She serves as a co-founding editor of Gazing Grain Press and teaches at the University of Alaska-Anchorage.

JULIA KOETS's poetry collection, *Hold Like Owls*, won the 2011 South Carolina Poetry Book Prize, judged by Nikky Finney. Her work has appeared or is forthcoming in *Indiana Review*, *The Los Angeles Review*, *The Carolina Quarterly*, and *the minnesota review*, among other journals. She is currently working on her Ph.D. in Creative Writing and Literature at the University of Cincinnati.

PETER LABERGE's work appears in *Beloit Poetry Journal*, *The Iowa Review*, *Sixth Finch*, *Colorado Review*, *Best New Poets 2014*, and *Indiana Review*, among other journals. He is the recipient of a fellowship from the Bucknell University Stadler Center for Poetry, the founder and editor-in-chief of *The Adroit Journal*, and an undergraduate student at the University of Pennsylvania. He lives in Philadelphia.

ELEANOR LERMAN is the author of numerous award-winning collections of poetry, short fiction, and novels, most recently, *Radiomen* (The Permanent Press, 2015). She is a National Book Award finalist, the recipient of the 2006 Lenore Marshall Poetry Prize from the Academy of American Poets, and has received both NEA and Guggenheim Fellowships.

ZACH LINGE is a graduate student at the University of Texas at San Antonio pursuing a master's degree in English and a graduate certificate in creative writing. A painter by training, Linge seeks to explore the visual territory between media—liminal spaces beyond canons that parallel his geographical experiences as a military child and his social territory as a queer.

KELLY MAGEE is the author of *Body Language* (UNT Press, 2006), *With Animal* (Black Lawrence Press, 2015), co-written with Carol Guess, and winner of University of North Texas's Katherine Anne Porter Prize for Short Fiction. Her work has appeared in *The Kenyon Review*, *Crazyhorse*,

Ninth Letter, Hayden's Ferry Review, Passages North, and other journals. She teaches at Western Washington University in Bellingham.

CAROLINE M. MAR lives, writes, and teaches in her hometown of San Francisco. She is a graduate of the M.F.A. Program for Writers at Warren Wilson College and an alumna of the Voices at VONA workshop, and her work has appeared in *As/Us, Shadowgraph, The Collagist, The Volta,* and other journals. She's currently revising her first collection of poems, *Special Education.*

KAITLIN LAMOINE MARTIN was raised by a community of writers in Kalamazoo, Michigan. She's been published in *Bellevue Literary Review, Borderlands: Texas Poetry Review,* and *Passages North,* among other journals. She owns a photography business, works for Communities In Schools, and spends hours thinking of new ways to entertain her dogs, Frida and Adam Lee Wags II.

EDUARDO MARTINEZ-LEYVA's poems have appeared in *Assaracus, The Journal, Nepantla: A Journal for Queer Poets of Color, Best New Poets 2015,* and other journals. He received his M.F.A. from Columbia University, where he was a teaching fellow. He grew up in El Paso, Texas, and currently lives in New York City. He is a CantoMundo Fellow.

LUCIEN DARJEUN MEADOWS's poetry has appeared in *West Branch, Hayden's Ferry Review,* and *Quarterly West.* An AWP Intro Journals Project winner, he has been nominated for the Pushcart Prize and received recognition from the Academy of American Poets. He lives in Fort Collins, Colorado.

RAJIV MOHABIR is the author of *The Taxidermist's Cut,* winner of Four Way Books Intro Prize in Poetry. His work has won awards such as the 2015 AWP Intro Journal Award and the 2015 Kundiman Prize. Currently he is pursuing a Ph.D. in English from the University of Hawai'i, where he teaches poetry and composition.

NANCY CAROL MOODY is the author of two collections of poetry, *Photograph with Girls* and *The House of Nobody Home* (FutureCycle Press, 2016). Her work has appeared in *The Southern Review, The Los Angeles Review, Phoebe,* and *The Journal.* She lives in Eugene, Oregon, with Marcela, her partner of 35 years.

BONNIE J. MORRIS is a women's studies professor on the faculty of both Georgetown and George Washington universities in Washington, D.C.

She is the author of 13 books, including three Lambda Literary Award finalists, *Eden Built by Eves*, *Girl Reel*, and *Revenge of the Women's Studies Professor*. Her next book, *The Disappearing L*, addresses the erasure of recent lesbian culture.

JIM NAWROCKI's work has appeared in *Poetry*, *Kyoto Journal*, *The Gay and Lesbian Review*, *Chelsea Station*, the website poetrydaily.com, and in the anthologies *The Place That Inhabits Us: Poems of the San Francisco Bay Watershed* (Sixteen Rivers Press, 2010) and *Art & Understanding: Literature from the First Twenty Years* (Black Lawrence Press, 2014).

GREG NICHOLL lives in Baltimore and works in publishing. His poetry has recently appeared or is forthcoming in *Crab Orchard Review*, *Ecotone*, *Mid-American Review*, *Natural Bridge*, *Post Road*, *Prairie Schooner*, *Smartish Pace*, and other journals.

JEFF OAKS's newest chapbook, *Mistakes with Strangers*, was published by Seven Kitchens Press in 2014. His poems and essays have appeared most recently in *Assaracus*, *At Length*, *Field*, *The Kenyon Review Online*, *Pittsburgh Poetry Review*, and *Creative Nonfiction*. He teaches writing at the University of Pittsburgh.

CHRISTOPHER PHELPS studied poetry by way of physics and philosophy, but Dickinson and the dictionary were his first loves. His poems appear in magazines including *Boston Review*, *Colorado Review*, and *The Kenyon Review*, and in the anthology *Collective BRIGHTNESS: LGBTIQ Poets on Faith, Religion & Spirituality*.

C. RUSSELL PRICE is an Appalachian genderqueer punk poet living in Chicago. They hold a B.A. from the University of Virginia and an M.F.A. from Northwestern University. Their chapbook *Tonight We Fuck The Trailer Park Out Of Each Other* will be published by Sibling Rivalry Press in June 2016. They work with *The Offing* and teach creative writing at Northwestern.

CHRISTINA QUINTANA is a writer and theater artist with Cuban and Louisiana roots. Her plays and musicals have been developed and produced in Atlanta, New Orleans, and New York City, and her poetry is published in *First Class Literary Magazine*, and *EMOTIVE FRUITION + Radiolab: Elemental Poetry for the Masses!*, and is forthcoming in *Raspa Magazine*. She is a proud former Lambda Literary Foundation Fellow in Fiction.

JAYME RINGLEB grew up in upstate South Carolina and Friuli-Venezia Giulia, Italy. He holds an M.F.A. from the University of Oregon and is currently a Ph.D. student in poetry at Florida State University. Jayme is the recipient of scholarships to the Sewanee Writers' Conference and the Lambda Literary Writers Retreat, a Fishtrap Fellowship, and prizes from the University of Oregon.

KRISTEN RINGMAN is a bisexual deaf writer, traveler, mother, and sailor. She writes multi-cultural lyrical fiction and poetry inspired by her persistent wanderings to far-off places. Her first novel, *Makara*, a Lambda Literary finalist in Debut Fiction, was published in 2012 by Handtype Press. She received her M.F.A. from Goddard College in 2008.

ALLEN SALERNO teaches in the English department at Auburn University. His poems have most recently appeared in *Assaracus*.

STEVEN SANCHEZ has received fellowships from CantoMundo and the Lambda Literary Foundation. He holds an M.F.A. in Creative Writing from Fresno State University and teaches at Fresno City College. His poems have appeared or are forthcoming in *Crab Creek Review*, *Word Riot*, *The Cossack Review*, and other journals.

IVAN SEINDERS, born in Tulsa, Oklahoma, writes fiction and poetry. He is currently a student and hopes to attend college before pursuing a career in either journalism or psychology.

SU SMALLEN is the author of six collections of poetry. Her first book, *Weight of Light,* was nominated for the Pushcart Press Editors' Book Award, and *Buddha, Proof* was a finalist for the Minnesota Book Award. She has two books forthcoming: *You This Close* with Red Dragonfly Press, and *de Kooning Snow* with Green Writers Press.

NOAH STETZER is a graduate of the M.F.A. Program for Writers at Warren Wilson College and a scholarship recipient for the Lambda Literary Retreat for Emerging LGBT Writers and the the Bread Loaf Writer's Conference. He was a winner of the 2015 Christopher Hewitt Award for Poetry and the 39th New Millennium Award for Poetry. Born and raised in Pittsburgh, Pennsylvania, he now lives in the Washington, D.C., area.

ALICE STINETORF holds an M.F.A. from the University of Arkansas, where she now teaches in the Department of English. Her work has appeared in publications such as *Post Road Magazine, Best of Ohio Short Stories, Surreal South, Yalobusha Review*, and *Harpur Palate*. Her honors include an Arkansas Arts Council fellowship for short-story writing.

LEE COLIN THOMAS lives and writes in Minneapolis, Minnesota. His poems have appeared in *Poet Lore, Salamander, The Gay and Lesbian Review Worldwide, Water~Stone Review, Midwestern Gothic, Pilgrimage, The Nassau Review*, and other journals.

ARISA WHITE received her M.F.A. from the University of Massachusetts, Amherst. She's a Cave Canem fellow and the author of *Post Pardon, Hurrah's Nest*, and *A Penny Saved*. The regional representative for *Nepantla: A Journal of Queer Poets of Color*, She is a B.F.A. faculty advisor at Goddard College. Forthcoming in October 2016 is *you're the most beautiful thing that happened* from Augury Books.

MAYA WHITE-LURIE wrote her first poem at age eight, and her writing has made its way into *Permafrost, Amendment Literary and Art Journal*, and *Quail Bell Magazine*. She currently lives in Richmond, Virginia.

GENEVIEVE N. WILLIAMS is a poet living and working in Omaha, Nebraska. Her work has been nominated for a Pushcart Prize, and has appeared or is forthcoming in *Plainsongs, burntdistrict, Lavender Review*, and other journals. She facilitates Omaha Writers Group, a weekly writing workshop open to the public, and is a teaching artist for Nebraska Writers Collective.

DEVON BROWNING grew up in a small town in southeastern Wisconsin. She attended the University of Wisconsin-La Crosse, earning dual degrees in Art and English Literature. Since moving to San Diego in 2009, she has had her work featured on the covers of *CityBeat Magazine* and *Adrienne: A Poetry Journal of Queer Women*. She currently paints out of La Bodega Galley and Studios in Barrio Logan, San Diego.

A. GANNON is a self-taught author and artist from Oklahoma.

ASHLEY INGUANTA is a writer and photographer driven by landscape and place. She is the author of three collections: *The Way Home* (Dancing Girl Press), *For The Woman Alone* (Ampersand Books), and *Bomb* (forthcoming from Ampersand Books). Her work has appeared in *PANK*, *The Rumpus*, *Bartleby Snopes*, *Adrienne: A Poetry Journal of Queer Women*, *OCHO*, and other literary spaces. She is also the Art Director of *SmokeLong Quarterly*.

DAVID MONDEDEU, originally from Houston, Texas, is a photographer residing in Madrid, Spain. He has published *Sonnets of 40 Winters and 40 Springs*, *From the East-Light*, and *Further South than Planned*.

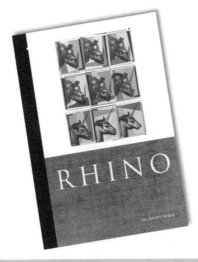